Table of Contents

High Heels 'N Oil Rigs

Beverley Jones

Joyce Anne
Publications

Acknowledgments:

Front Cover Photo: Jim Maxwell
Photo Enhancement & Cover Design:
  Stuart Bish Photography/Design
Cover Printed by: Pacific Image Color
Printed and Bound by: Hanson Printing

Printed and Bound in Canada
  First Printing   1995
  This Edition   1998

ISBN 0-9683822-1-5

Books by Beverley Jones:

HIGH HEELS 'N' OIL RIGS, 1995
WHEN WE WERE LITTLE KIDS (Memoirs), 1997
TERROR IN THE OIL PATCH, 1998

Joyce Anne Publications

381 Norton Street
Penticton, BC V2A 4H9
Tel: (250) 490-9639
Fax: (250) 492-7278

Dedication

This book is dedicated to my sons—Jim, Doug, Keith and Murray—and their families. None was ever too tired, too busy or too bored to listen, read, edit or talk about "Mom's" book which took a very long time to write. They always responded with honest, constructive criticism when a subject came up that I was unsure about. They, like me, always knew I would get this book published, and finally that has become a reality.

My good friends Sallie and Lorraine, who never doubted I would one day publish my great adventure, gave me the confidence and gentle "push" into writing about my life on the oil rigs. And my first newspaper editor, Doug Caston, often said, "you probably were a writer in your previous life so get with it and just do it."

Finally I want to thank the bold, brave men I call "rig hands" who provided me with so much to write about in that fabulous adventure into a completely new way of life out there in 1970s Oil Patch in the northwestern Canadian wilderness.

The incidents described in this book, some hilarious, some ridiculous and some very sad, are based on my experiences. To protect the identity of certain characters, some names of people and places have been changed.

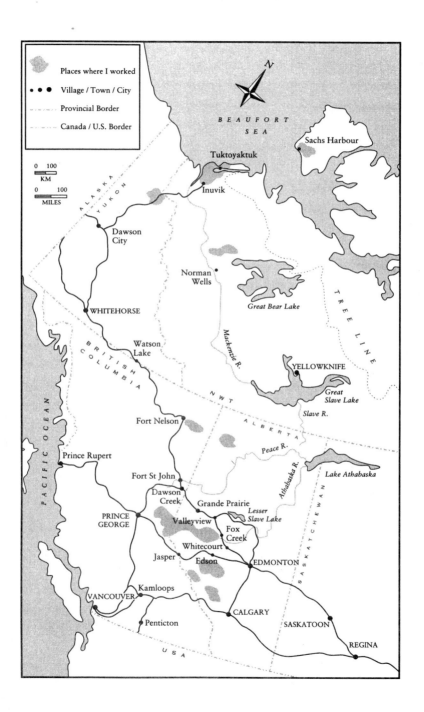

Places where I worked

Village / Town / City

Provincial Border

Canada / U.S. Border

0   100
KM

0   100
MILES

N

BEAUFORT
SEA

Sachs Harbour

Tuktoyaktuk

Inuvik

ALASKA

YUKON

Dawson
City

Norman
Wells

Great Bear Lake

TREE LINE

WHITEHORSE

Watson
Lake

BRITISH
COLUMBIA

Mackenzie R.

YELLOWKNIFE

Great
Slave Lake

NWT

ALBERTA

Slave R.

Fort Nelson

PACIFIC OCEAN

Prince Rupert

Peace R.

Athabaska R.

Lake Athabaska

Fort St John

Dawson
Creek

Grande Prairie

Lesser
Slave Lake

SASKATCHEWAN

PRINCE
GEORGE

Valleyview

Fox
Creek

Jasper

Whitecourt

Edson

EDMONTON

Kamloops

VANCOUVER

CALGARY

Penticton

SASKATOON

USA

REGINA

Prologue

Woman in Distress

THE WOMAN WAS COLD, TIRED and very frightened. She reached across the seat of the truck for her cigarettes, extracted one and felt around for her lighter. She didn't take her eyes off the road; she didn't dare. The road was a sea of mud with a swift-flowing creek on one side and a hundred miles of muskeg on the other.

How much further it was to her destination was anyone's guess. She had passed the estimated mileage two hours ago. A warning kept gnawing at her mind: "Never, never underestimate the distance when the information comes down from head office."

She could have been anywhere in the awesome wilderness of northern Alberta and British Columbia. It all looked the same. It is a wilderness that looks so beautiful from the air but is cold and frightening and so terribly lonely when one is alone in it.

She had been driving since sunup, and darkness was settling in. It was late autumn — a time when evening comes early in this part of the world. Her mind was busy with driving, but there they were again: those nagging thoughts that kept creeping into her mind about leaving this type of work.

"I must quit this job. I have to leave this life behind me . . . get on with my life somewhere else . . . away from this awesome, endless wilderness, this constant exposure to danger, the loneliness and the roads. They're not roads! They're trails . . . just trails pushed out of the bush with a cat. Roads!"

The woman had just taken her "long change", her week out of camp, and was returning to yet another tour-of-duty which she vowed would be her last. She was tired of living in two worlds, and she had no intention of ending up like that geologist or the camp attendant in Zama. Eaten by a bear. Carried away and buried by that horrible creature which would return to complete its grisly feast.

" Oh . . . I must get out of this job. I must. I have to, for my own peace of mind."

She glanced at the fuel gauge. It was nearly empty. Terror rose up in her throat again. She had filled up in Fox Creek, and either her gauge wasn't working or the gas attendant didn't fill her tank.

"If I run out of fuel, I'll have to spend the night out here. There won't be another vehicle over this road tonight, I don't think. I've got to get a hold of myself. I must not panic."

She let the truck come to a complete stop right in the middle of the trail. She had to settle her nerves, get out and walk around the vehicle, stretch her legs, get some air, clear her mind, and then get on with the trip. She had to pull herself together. Lately, this fretting and terror had started occurring on every trip back into a new location. A new camp, a new location, used to be fun. It wasn't anymore. It was time to leave.

She pulled on a pair of long rubber boots and stepped out into the mud. She slowly walked around her pickup truck, inspecting the tires and straightening the side mirrors which had been yanked out of place by overhanging branches. She glanced into the bushes that grew along the roadside. It was already dark in the forest. She looked down the muddy trail that lay ahead and then at the muddy ruts she had just driven over. She shook her head, climbed back into the truck, rolled the window down, and silently watched the muddy water slip by.

There wasn't a sound out there in that vast wilderness. She marvelled at that for a long time. It was overwhelming. Nothing made a noise out there. Not even the friendly caw of a raven or the lonely call of a loon was heard to ease the ache in her being. The woman had loved the wilderness once, but she didn't any more. It was too frightening. The only sound she could hear was the steady beat of her heart. She was about to start the truck when she heard a sound.

Yes! She heard it again . . . a twig snapping. Her head shot around and without realizing it she was rolling up the window. Her hand was on the keys in the ignition, but her fingers froze on them. A huge brown bear lumbered out of the bushes and moved across the road not ten feet in front of her truck. The hump on its shoulder told her it was a grizzly. She watched in total horror as it lifted its snout and swung its head from side to side. Long patches of slobber clung to its side and front leg.

When the grizzly reached the water's edge it stood up on its hind legs and looked around in all directions. A small cry escaped from the terrified woman. She stared

3

at the creature as it lay down in the swift water and let the current take it across to the far side where it climbed out of the water, shook itself and entered the darkening forest.

The woman fought to control her fear. She must not scream. The terror was strangling her. She felt tears sting her eyes and then run freely down her face. She hugged herself to control the shaking and sat quietly until she was able to drive. Then she started the truck and drove away from that awful place.

After another half-hour, she saw a light. She began to cry again. She was very grateful. She would be safe this time. She refused to let her mind dwell on the grizzly. She drove carefully into camp and parked her truck.

As she gathered her gear, she talked to herself. She knew her terror wasn't entirely caused by that bear. It was the whole thing — the isolation, the dreadful loneliness, the roads, and the bears.

Yes, it was time to leave the rigs for good . . . .

Chapter One

High Heels 'n' Oil Rigs

I LEFT THE OIL RIGS in 1979 — a lifetime ago . . . or so it seems. Now, when I read the chapters and notes I wrote in those early years, the memories come flooding back — memories which bring tears, smiles, and thoughts of some people I admire very much: the Canadian roughnecks and rig hands. That era in the Western Canadian oil patch is over, but few people know very much about its rich history. This book is about the actual drill sites and camp sites which were so far away from everything. It was a wilderness beyond comprehension — a place where no one lived and where only oil pioneers, roughnecks and rig hands dared to venture.

I was among the early group of women who went out into this wilderness to work in rig camps that were not designed to house women cooks. We made the best of an impossible situation and were rewarded to see conditions change. Change was slow, but it did and it continues to occur. The isolation now is not quite like what it was "back then." There are good roads where muddy trails used to be. There is satellite TV. There is a telephone system to relay information around the world. The oil industry must be credited with opening up this vast country, building roads and pipelines and modernizing the drilling for oil and gas.

Life in the drilling camps is a mystery to most Canadians. I'm sure many people must wonder how that gas, down at the corner service station, gets there. There is a whole world out there that few people know. I would like to give you a woman's perspective of that world.

I entered my new "career" as an oil rig cook looking for excitement and adventure. I got multitudes of both, but I got caught up in a lot of other experiences too. I had no idea of the redneck attitude that existed in the oil patch then, and to some extent still exists today. I'm not saying a redneck attitude is all wrong; some of my best friends, including my own brother, are rednecks. I want to tell you about the way women were treated in the "patch" in those early years. It was pretty trying at times. Many of my relatives, including one of my sons, still work in the oil patch, and from what I see and read, the oil patch has changed dramatically.

New technology had arrived in many areas even before I left the rigs. New rigs were built to dig deeper holes, and I'm told they make a rig worker's job a lot safer and a little easier. However, rig work is still very dangerous, especially in Canada, where a lot of drilling is done under cruel winter conditions. Canada's Arctic has some pretty long cold, dark days. Extremely cold winds blow most of the time.

I had a rude awakening on my very first trip to an oil rig in late September of 1970. I was driven out to the International Airport, south of Edmonton, where I stood around in the late September chill with about 55 other people — all men. I endured a lot of stares but not one smile or greeting. I spent the whole day in that same company, and not once did any one of those men speak to me except to say, "Hey. You, lady. Ya forgot your gear."

We stopped in Norman Wells to deliver freight and to drop off some men. While they were unloading, they damaged the door of the aircraft and we had to wait until they got it fixed. It took three hours. When we landed in Inuvik, we were driven to a lake, or some body of water, and I had to board a plane that was bobbing up and down with huge waves slapping all around us. I was terrified! I climbed aboard, found a seat, and strapped myself in. Then I glanced out the window, which was splashed with water, and saw my bags still sitting on the dock. I heard that voice again:

"Ya forgot your gear, Lady."

Yes, I had to get out there and drag in my bags. Believe me, it wasn't easy to stand up straight and look smart with that plane rocking around in the wash and with all those guys watching me. There were still no smiles — just disgust on their faces.

We landed across the bay from Tuktoyuktuk, and I followed the men into a camp made up of trailers, doors and hallways. I learned later that it was a base camp for an oil company and was much larger than the drilling camp which was my destination. A base camp is made up of many trailers with hallways and double-doored entrances. The latter are used to keep out the cold and, I believe, to trap lemmings. Every time I ever attempted to enter or leave a kitchen while working in the Arctic it seemed there were lemmings cowering in a corner. I screamed every single time I saw them.

We hung around that huge camp for a long time, and several times a man yelled out numbers. The people who corresponded to these numbers were told to board a plane or chopper. Five or six guys would grab their bags and run out through that maze of doors and entrances. Soon my number was called, and I ran out behind the guys to a little chopper which sat on the pad just outside camp. I climbed in last and, you guessed it, I forgot my bags again. This time a very nice young man picked them up and threw them into the chopper with a stern warning: "Look after your own gear lady." And then we were off. It was thrilling — my first chopper flight. But the landscape was dreary and barren . . . just miles of rolling tundra with quite a lot of blowing snow. That part of the Arctic is treeless.

Off in the distance I could see what I assumed was our rig camp. We flew directly over the rig site and dropped down right beside camp. Men came running to the chopper pad, and the faces of the five men with whom I had been travelling all day broke into smiles as they grabbed their bags and climbed down to greetings and guffaws. I grabbed my bag and dragged it to the door. I tried to be very dignified and careful as I lowered myself onto the step. My high heel caught in the wire mesh, and I fell right into the arms of a tall, handsome man who was about my age. It was the last time I wore high heels and a skirt into an oil rig camp.

The Prince Charming who broke my fall turned out to be the tool push, or rig boss . . . and a childhood acquaintance. This made my first tour of duty into the oil patch a lot easier.

My work on the oil rigs was a far cry from what I had been doing for the first 20 years of my working life. I was 44 years old when I made my first trip into the Arctic. I was single and attractive, or so I thought, and I was looking for adventure. I wanted to make some money, to try a new job, and to get out of my rut.

I had worked as a beautician in hair salons for years. Then I had bought one in Calgary and had made a living for myself and for my four sons while they finished high school. At this point, I sold my salon and we moved to Vancouver, where my kids and I enjoyed that beautiful city during the "hippie" era. I was managing large salons for a major department store in Vancouver when I accepted a transfer to Edmonton. My kids were all grown up and scattered, and I was sort of looking forward to returning to my home province. All my children were born in Alberta, and I still had family there.

Within three months I knew I must have left my mind back in Vancouver to have accepted a transfer to Edmonton. I didn't even have a block heater in my car.

I worked hard to forget the coast and the mild weather. Every morning, I dreaded going out into that deep freeze, where cars spouted exhaust and where the roads were slippery.

Then one day my stepsister dropped in en route from Sable Island where she had been cooking for a drilling company. During the evening we discussed wages. I was astonished to learn that she made more than three times what I was making, and she only had two staff members to supervise: a cook's helper and a camp attendant.

That was for me. Great money and an adventure to boot, I thought. The very next day I went to the catering company that she had suggested and was hired on the spot. I had never been in an industrial kitchen before in my life. I had no idea where all that grease went that I had seen grill cooks scraping off their grills in diners . . . until I was walking in it.

I had a lot to learn!

Chapter Two

Shop Talk

THE OIL PATCH is a very unusual place to work. The terminology used is in a class by itself. The pecking order is extremely important. To gain an understanding of some of this terminology, it's necessary to know what goes on during a regular day on an oil rig and rig camp. I gained all my knowledge of what went on out at the rig by listening, over and over and over, to conversations around the meal table.

The whole operation is usually miles from nowhere, accessed by a terrible road, and the drilling takes place through a swampy muskeg. It has always been a mystery to me how a geologist or seismic crew always decides there is gas or oil right in the middle of the biggest muskeg in an area.

The man in charge of the operation is called a "tooly," tool push, pusher, rig boss, dad, or quite a few other names when he isn't around. The tool push is an experienced rig hand who has worked his way up the ladder from a lowly dummy roughneck. He is responsible for a multi-million dollar operation and for a crew of up to 38 or more people, including the cooks. His word is final. He's the boss, and he answers only to his

superiors at head office in Edmonton, Calgary or elsewhere. He's probably a high school drop-out, but he's
smart as a whip. His main priorities are to run a "smooth"
operation, to keep a good crew, and to try and get the
cook, or her helper, into his bed.

A roughneck is the newest rig hand on the job. He
gets all the dirty jobs to do. When he is first hired, he is
called a dummy roughneck, and he helps the regular
roughneck with tripping duties on the drilling platform.

The roughneck is also the guy who travels to and
from the camp site twice a day to pick up the meal box
for the workers. For lunch, the cook usually sends out
soup, sandwiches, pickles, green salad, coleslaw, potato
salad, cake, pie, cookies, and doughnuts. Drinks of all
types are left in the doghouse fridge. Rig hands can eat
huge meals, especially in the winter. For the evening meal
there are two choices of meat, including steak twice a
week, potatoes, two vegetables, biscuits, homemade
dinner rolls, and leftover pickles and salads. For dessert
there are two or three choices of pie, cake, cinnamon
buns and cookies. Fresh fruit is always available in the
doghouse fridge. Tea, coffee, and hot chocolate comes
with every meal. It is never certain that all the food gets
all the way to the drilling rig. Roughnecks have been
known to eat an entire pan of buns in the short time it
takes to get from the camp kichen to the rig.

The new roughneck also performs any other menial
job that comes up during the course of his shift. If the
driller can't think of a job at the moment, there is always
drilling mud to be unloaded. The roughneck unloads the
bags of mud into the mud shack: a special place that

keeps the mud dry. Ordering a dummy roughneck around is great sport for the crew on duty.

This roughneck is the target of every practical joke imaginable. If he falls asleep in the mud shack, he will find the soles of his boots painted when he wakes up. If he removes his boots for a more comfortable sleep, he will often find them nailed to the floor. He is often asked to find a sky-hook and will spend the entire day looking for this mythical tool. If he can cope with all this fun and games, he will one day become a real roughneck. Then he will be promoted to motorman and learn the mysteries of the huge motors that generate the power for the operation.

There is usually a separate power plant at the campsite, and the motorman is responsible for keeping it serviced. If he fails to fuel it up and it stops, all hell breaks loose in camp. Everyone is out to get the "stupid son-of-a-bitch" who forgot to fuel up the power plant.

When the motorman learns his craft, he will eventually be allowed to climb the rig tower to grease the mechanism and to see how he manages heights. He will gradually learn to work up top and to do all the other jobs that the derrickman does, both on the ground and in his lofty perch atop the drilling rig.

The derrickman is sort of like God out there. He braves the cold winds and is exposed to the worst kinds of rig accidents. His is a very dangerous job. He is strapped in at all times. If he fails to observe company rules about belting himself in properly — and some derrickmen can be very negligent about this — he can be knocked out of his perch by an improperly-handled stand of pipe. If a rig blows out or catches on fire, the derrickman must escape via a thick cable which is fastened at one end to the stand where he works, strung down to the edge of the platform and secured to a post. If the derrickman isn't blown to bits, he will fasten himself into a crude seat, which hangs from the drilling platform, and slide down the cable to safety. This escape route is called a "Geronimo." A test ride down this terrifying contraption has been turned down by most cooks who work on the rig camps, including myself.

When the derrickman learns to drill, there is a conflict between him and the existing driller on the rig. One of them has to go if they want to keep moving up the ladder to become tool push. Usually, it's the new driller who looks for another rig to drill on. He does this on his week out, when he talks an unsuspecting tool push on another rig into believing that he has at least two years experience drilling. When the boom was on during the '70s, it wasn't unusual to have a whole crew whose combined experience totaled about two years.

Many times during my ten years on the rigs, I was almost convinced that a good rig hand was judged on his ability to tell stories. In the "good old days," before satellite TV, a good storyteller was indispensable in an isolated camp. In the metal trailers where we worked, even our radios didn't work very well, so we sort of had to create our own fun. Telling stories was by far the most popular entertainment. It is an art that is mastered only after hours of practice.

On most rig camps throughout the western Canadian oil patch, there is an elite bunch of men who sit around and drink coffee a lot. These men take their meals in camp, and the cooks get to know them before, and

probably better than, anyone else. There is st
in my mind about whether these men are really ne
a drilling operation, as most cooks could pro
handle the job quite easily. I'm referring primarily to
engineers, the geologists, the mud men, the forklii
operators, the cat skinners and a few others. This crew
has been known to do some work, sometime, somewhere, but their primary function is to play cards, drink
coffee and tease the camp staff.

I mustn't forget to mention one of the most important of this elite crew — the water hauler, sometimes
known as the "water buffalo". He is the man who hauls
water in a tank truck, if the camp doesn't have a well. He
also supplies the rig with extra water if the crew is "stuck
in the hole" or has any other emergencies. If the emergency is a cave-in or a fracture, where a "fishing trip"
becomes necessary, the water hauler becomes quite busy.

Normally, however, a water hauler doesn't have
much to do, so he sits around drinking coffee, tasting
pastries and flattering the cooks. If the cooks run out of
water, the water hauler makes himself very scarce. He
won't be found until the tank in camp is full to running
over. He eventually hears, through the camp grapevine,
that the cooks have simmered down, and he bravely
strolls into camp to flatter the cooks on their excellent
pastry, their slim figures or their new hairdos. He will
probably go on and on with his flattery until he is told to
shut up. Then he has to agree to take the cooks on a trip
down to the creek where he loads his water tank, just for
a drive and a few minutes out of the kitchen.

It was on one of these trips that a water hauler
made my first slingshot for me. I eventually used that

weapon to shoot a light out in a lounge in Edson, Alberta. But that is a story which will be told later.

When I was in the oil patch, the engineer was an old rig hand who either worked his way up the ladder from tool push or was talked into the job by an oil company executive. The engineer and the geologist are the oil company representatives on site. The tool push runs the drilling rig and camp, but the engineer and geologist are top dogs at the drill site. The drilling company is hired by the oil company to drill the well, so in essence the oil company is the *real* top dog. The lease where the drilling is taking place also belongs to the oil company.

On the average drilling rig in western Canada, engineers and geologists spend a lot of time driving between the rig and camp. They drink an awful lot of coffee, are usually easy to please in the food department, and play a great game of gin rummy. These men are referred to as "top brass" by those of us who are very low down in the pecking order of rig life.

A common courtesy on a rig camp is to listen to these men tell of the terrible roads they've travelled, - the worst in the oil patch, of course, the long stretches they've spent in camp, and the huge bears they've run off a lease or shot in self defence, of course. Naturally, they're also the best fisherman around when there's a fishing job to be done — on or off the rig.

They are also among the best storytellers in camp. These talents only serve to support my theory that engineers, geologists, and tool pushers do not have a great deal to do on a drilling rig — other than to perfect their story-telling skills over coffee and gin rummy.

A tour of duty is much more pleasant when ͺ pusher, engineer and geologist work well togethͺ most of the best camps I was on, they were old buͺ who had worked together for years. These friendshͺps helped to make life more pleasant on a rig.

Geologists were a different breed of cat. In those early days, they were the only university-educated men in the rig camp. Therefore, they were thought to be rather odd. Why should anyone go to university when they can learn it on the rig?

The geologist has an important role to play. He determines what kind of drilling bit should be used for drilling, according to the kind of rock formation they're drilling through. He also determines whether the crew should continue drilling or whether a service team should be brought in for further testing. Even though they have these important jobs, it is still my firm belief that those in higher positions on a rig site have so little to do they have time to practice that most important of all leisure pastimes — playing gin rummy.

The crew who work the graveyard shift, 8 p.m to 8 a.m. sleep right through lunch but show up sometime during the afternoon to watch the "soaps" or an old movie on tape.

The cooks quite often sit at the table and eat with this crew during supper, and I suppose it's from those conversations that I learned just what goes on at a rig. We would be treated to in-depth conversations of mud viscosity, drilling bits, tripping, fishing - not stream fishing, and the complete stupidity of the most recent arrival in camp who had the audacity to call himself a roughneck.

Within one year my language slowly deteriorated from pretty decent to downright terrible. The mark of a true rig hand is the "colourful" language he uses. Since I left the rigs, I have continually tried to clean up my language but have failed miserably.

It was during my third year on the rigs that I realized my helper and I were becoming quite expert at knowing just how to operate a drilling rig. Take fishing, for example. During my first two years on the oil rigs, I thought they were talking about trout fishing. Then I met a fisherman who didn't have his fishing pole. He explained, in detail, just what he did on a rig and why it was so expensive to have him around.

A fisherman is called in when there is either a fracture or something lost down the drilling hole. All foreign objects must be removed before drilling can continue. This is always a crucial time on a rig because it causes an enormously expensive delay. Besides being costly, a fishing job or a fracture or being stuck in the hole is very hard on everyone, including the cooks. Everyone in camp is on edge and the men curse and swear a lot. There are other reasons for all the swearing and cursing but I'm not quite sure what they are; there are a few things I never learned out there.

Mixing mud is a highly technical job. The drilling mixture must be a certain viscosity which is determined by the geologist and/or mudmen, according to the formation they are drilling through. A special type of mud is imported for drilling purposes. Tons of mud are used before a well is completed.

When the drilling is completed, all the mud used during the entire operation is drained into a huge sump and left for a service rig and crew who come in after the drilling rig leaves. The site is then drained and covered back over according to strict environmental regulations. A drill site, immediately after a well has been dug, is a horrible sight.

A regular crew consists of five men. On some exploration wells, or if a company is authorized by the oil company, they will have six men on a crew. Sometimes there will be an assistant driller and sometimes there will be a lease hound, usually a student or someone's son or brother, who is a "gopher," or dummy roughneck. He goes for everything, all day long.

There are always two rig crews in camp at all times who work alternating 12-hour shifts. The camp staff – cook, cook's helper and camp attendant – also works 12- to 14-hour days. The whole crew works for two weeks in and then a week out, called a "long change."

Chapter Three

Safety

WHEN I FIRST WENT OUT to a rig in the Arctic, there were three crews in camp at all times. This was a disaster! One tool push summed it all up when he commented that the crews have eight hours to work, eight hours to sleep and eight hours to bitch.

The short shifts were especially difficult for the cooks because there were always so many men around camp. And most camps did not have recreation trailers. There were many disputes over card games, fishing, girlfriends on the outside, and anything else that could be turned into an argument. It was a relief for us all when the "brass" made the decision to change to the two-crew, 12-hour shift system. This way, there was always one crew on their week out.

Long change usually occured every second Thursday. The rig hands came off a 12-hour shift at 8 a.m., hurried into camp, grabbed their gear, which was probably packed before they went out on duty the evening before, and then headed into the kitchen for a snack or a coffee. It was not unusual for them to leave without even a cup of coffee, but a lot of them stood around the coffee urn discussing where they would meet when they got to town. Town meant the first settlement reached after travelling dangerous muddy or dusty gravel rig roads, sometimes for 60 miles or more at speeds far too fast for road conditions.

Driving by a bar is almost unheard of in drilling areas; nearly all rig hands pull into a hotel bar just to see who else might show up from other rigs in that area. It is a time for visiting, chatting, bragging and drinking before continuing on home. This is a very dangerous practice and a time when accidents occur. There are a few rig workers who drive straight home but they are few and far between.

It is this practice that most good tool pushers were trying to deal with when I left the rigs. It wasn't an easy issue. One very responsible tool push told his workers, when they were hired, that they would be required to eat, shower and rest for four hours after their last shift before they would be considered due for long change. Many rig workers balked at that and laughed at the push, but they were told they wouldn't have a job when they returned if they didn't abide by the rules.

This is still a very touchy issue in the oil patch today. Workers are not unionized and probably never will be, but leaving a job with 14 gruelling shifts behind them, and with no sleep for at least 12 hours, to travel over dangerous roads is a recipe for disaster.

This situation also applies to the wireline and other testing companies who go out to a rig to perform their duties. It is not unusual for a testing crew to be in camp for five days, receiving very little sleep, complete a job, and then be expected at another rig as soon as possible. These men are expensive to have on a lease, and when another engineer is screaming for the testers, it leaves little time for rest. These are just some of the reasons why so many rig workers get killed upon coming to or leaving a rig site.

A very thoughtful engineer, who really cared about his men, told me about a safety seminar he attended in Banff. Most of these issues were brought forward for discussion, but not a lot was ever done to solve them. It seems a lot of accidents occur coming into camp and during the first shift. There could be different explanations for these accidents. A rig worker might be in love, and his girlfriend, or wife, might not want him to go back to his job. There might have been an ultimatum before he left her. Or the rig hand might have had a quarrel with his wife or lady friend, he might have relived the quarrel all the way back to camp, and his mind may not have been on his work when he got onto the platform. And, of course, there is the most obvious reason of all: the rig hand might have been drunk. In the ten years I spent on the rigs I would guestimate that more than half of the crew members arriving in camp had been drinking and had had very little sleep even though they knew they would have to go on duty immediately upon arrival in camp.

The banter around the coffee urn or breakfast table tells the story: "Yeah . . . do you know who we ran into at Fox Creek? Had his new wife along.

She's so pretty we all hung around just to look at her . . . only had a couple, I think, or three . . . . "

And the same applies when they are leaving camp on long change: "Meet ya at Fox City. I'm buying . . . it's my birthday." It's the rig hands way of doing things.

After long change rig hands are supposed to be in camp, dressed and ready to take over the "short shift", 4 p.m. until midnight. If the roads are bad, and if the two crews get on well, then the crew out at the rig will carry on without too much grumbling. The time is usually traded for another error in getting in on time. When it gets to be 6 or 7 p.m. and no crew has shown up, then everyone is either worried or angry. The push is on the mobile trying to find out where they are. He shares any new information with those in the camp kitchen and then goes out to the rig to update the crew on duty who are working well into the next shift.

Occasionally, this wait has a terrible ending. No amount of worry or anger can heal the hurt that sometimes occurs. I vividly remember one of my favourite tool pushers who was about at his wits end. The incoming crew was over two hours late, and his anger had turned to worry and dread.

The push had a feeling something was terribly wrong, but something had to be done to relieve the crew on duty who were already working into the next shift. He poured a cup of coffee and then forgot where he left it. He talked to himself then he sat down with his head in his hands to think out what had to be done. Then he jumped up and grinned at my assistant Shelly. "Wanna be a roughneck?"

We stopped our work in stunned silence. We both looked at him as though he'd lost his mind. "Sure, I mean it. I can probably get the water hauler to work derrick.

He worked derrick last year on this very rig. And the forklift operator, what's his name, will probably help us out on the platform with you, Shelly. I'll drill. OK? It's all set. Oh yeah, you girls'll have to round up some safety duds for Shell there. I saw a pretty small pair of safety boots in Harold's room." (Harold was the camp attendant, or campy.) "Go get'm girls." He was grinning as he left for his office to change clothes for a shift on the drill stick.

We headed for Harold's room with Shelly tagging behind. "You sure you don't mind if I go out there, Bev?"

So many things went through my mind then. What if she gets hurt, loses a finger, a toe, a hand . . . but I knew she wanted to go.

"OK, sure Shelly, why not. You've been wanting a chance like this for a long time . . . I'm sorry this chance didn't come with some preparation — like proper clothes and work boots . . . ".

We all knew they were tripping, so they needed a full crew. The tool push had to drill. The water hauler, an old derrick hand, agreed to go up the derrick. And the forklift operator said he would work with Shelly on the drilling platform as a roughneck. The motorman who had been on duty said he would work with them through that shift. He was sure the incoming crew would arrive at any moment. The push was very relieved to have a full crew and nodded his thanks to the rig hands as the other four went into camp.

This whole arrangement caused a lot of concern to all of us. First, our tool push, who worked for the drilling company, was using oil company personnel. Furthermore, even though these men were experienced people, they had not worked on a rig platform for a long time. We didn't know if they'd be insured, and what if . . . . There was also the worry that the work in the kitchen would be too hard on me and my camp attendant. Finally, we were all worried for my helper's safety.

But Shelly wasn't worried about anything. She called us all a bunch of worrywarts and laughed at us. She had tried to hire on as a roughneck every time one didn't show up, but we were working for a company of rednecks who just wouldn't allow women on the drilling platform.

Our tool push was of a far different opinion. He thought that if a woman could do the job well, she should have the job. Shelly was very dependable, a hard worker, got along well with everyone and she was strong. But she had one serious drawback: she was only five foot two inches tall and about 110 pounds.

We all ran around camp trying to find clothes that would fit her. She finally pulled on a pair of rig boots wearing seven pairs of socks so they would fit. Then we had a little crying jag as I pushed her out the door on her way to the rig. I warned her to be very careful and I shouted at the crew to take good care of her. They all said, "OK, OK, OK, all right!" I knew they would — she was the best helper I ever had, and the guys loved her and were very protective of her in camp.

Shelly grew up on a farm outside of Grande Prairie with six brothers and one sister. She knew how to work and how to handle men. And she was gorgeous with long red hair and a face like an angel. It was one of the few times I really worried about her. It was one of her happiest moments on the rig. At last she was going to be a roughneck and a roughneck made almost twice what we did. But this story doesn't end here.

Halfway into that shift, we got a call on the mobile. I answered it, as all available people were at the rig. All five members of the incoming crew had been in a car crash a few miles west of Beaverlodge, just west of the British Columbia-Alberta border. Two were killed outright, and three were taken to hospital in Grande Prairie with undetermined injuries. I sat at the mobile with this terrible news that I knew must be passed to our tool push immediately. I called to Harold, and we both shed a few tears as we walked slowly down to the rig site.

We spoke only to the push who nodded his head and went on with his work. We knew he would be down to camp as soon as they completed the trip. We walked back to an empty camp and slowly proceeded to make the evening meal. We knew it would have to be a good one because this crew was destined to work a very long shift.

This story had some very harsh lessons to give my helper, the crew for whom she worked so hard, and our tool push.

Because Shelly worked so well, the push asked her if she would continue working until he could get some help out from head office. We heard him on the mobile, but we were too busy to listen. Two men showed up to replace the water hauler and the forklift operator, but Shelly stayed on the job for three more days. She was delighted to be asked to stay on. We sat on her bed in the evening talking and wondering just how much money she would make and how much sooner she would be able to go back to school if she could stay on in that capacity.

Our tool push said that as far as he was concerned the job was hers. We went to bed on that happy note.

On the fourth day a new driller arrived, so our tool pusher could get on with his work. I could hear him in his office asking for another helper, and I also heard a terrible lot of shouting. Then I heard the receiver being slammed down, and the tool push stomped into the kitchen. "That bunch of rednecks in the office won't send out another cook's helper. They told me to get that woman off the rig platform and back into the kitchen, and then they said it was not company policy to hire women on their rigs." Our push was very angry. He went back into his office, and I heard a lot more shouting, but I was far too busy to listen. I was still short a helper.

Another roughneck appeared at our kitchen the following morning and was sent out to the rig. Shelly came back into camp, crying. Within two minutes we were both crying. We cursed a lot of oil patch brass that morning, but we gradually let it go.

We all settled back into our routines and rushed to answer the mobile many times during the days that followed. We got several updates on our crew who had been let out of the hospital and were mending at home. None of us could get out for the funerals of our friends, but we held a brief moment of silence at our dinner table.

The week went by and then it was payday. Shelly and I were very anxious to see how much money she made as a roughneck and how much of a bonus my campy and I would receive for doing Shelly's job. It was a sad letdown. We all got straight pay all the way through. We shed a few tears and then, as usual, I got mad.

I beckoned to Shelly to follow, and we marched down the hall to the push's office. He was still ranting and raving on the mobile, but he motioned us to enter. We both knew by the conversation that he knew about our pay cheques and was fighting on our behalf. He finally slammed the receiver down and turned around with his head in his hands. When he looked up at us, it was with great sorrow, and we knew it was genuine. He was one of the best guys in the oil patch. He treated us as equals and tried to do something about our low level of pay. We joined him in a strong drink of whisky and ran down every official in our head office.

Just when we thought it couldn't get any worse, it did. An official from our head office showed up to make sure our push put Shelly back into the kitchen and to see what other mess he could stir up. We were rude to him and didn't serve him a meal and he left after a short, loud argument with our tooly.

A few days later, when we were stowing gear into the canopy of my truck in preparation for our long change, the men who worked with Shelly out at the rig came out to wave good-bye and to remind us to be sure to come back and to be careful, just as they always did.

Then the water hauler came forward with an envelope and shoved it in Shelly's hand. It was stuffed full of cash, and a small note written in pencil said, "You sure did a good job, Shell. We sure would like to have you on our team. Hope this will make it up for the office creeps who didn't pay you. Some in there for Bev and Harold too. Ya all did a great job." There were no names, but it was obvious that every man in camp had contributed out of respect for us women, our campy and our tool pusher.

We left camp with a real good feeling, and yes, we did go back. There were good men on that rig. They couldn't do a lot about the redneck attitude at head office, but they tried.

I understand a lot of this attitude has changed now, and women are working on rig platforms. I do not know how it is working out, but I'm sure it wasn't easy for the first women in any job, trade or profession.

Chapter Four

Grizzly Valley

IF A PLACE CALLED GRIZZLY VALLEY brings visions of great big grizzly bears to mind, you're absolutely right. Apart from being one of the most isolated and forlorn places on the face of the earth, Grizzly Valley has a lot of bears — grizzly bears.

Grizzly Valley is located about one hundred miles southwest of Grande Prairie, Alberta. It is reached by a horrible trail — or road, as they were called back then. This trail was known as Monkman Pass.

A rich oil strike was discovered in that pass several years prior to the rush of drilling during the booming '70s. I was on one of the first rig camps sent into that area to resume the drilling. I believe the company I was working for at the time must have been punishing me for something. Otherwise they wouldn't have done that to me.

We drove in the first time, but after that all crews were flown in and out from Grande Prairie. Because it was in the foothills, the trail was at the mercy of the renowned Chinook winds that melted the snow and caused whole chunks of road to crumble into the steep ravines and gorges. It was a terrible place to work.

Rumour had it that a school teacher by the name of Monkman, from Nanton, southern Alberta, drove a Ford car through that pass during the early 1930s. That incredible feat was supposed to have taken place, but in my opinion, Mr. Monkman couldn't have gone through that pass with a mule team, let alone a Ford car.

I won't dwell on the first trip into that valley, but I do remember seeing a fuel truck, still smoldering in a steep ravine, when we reached the part of the road that wasn't there any more. We performed a sort of portage with our groceries and other emergency supplies across the gorge, where the road had been partially washed out. We struggled, pushed and dragged the boxes over the narrow strip of road which had a mountain on one side and a deep gorge on the other. Small rocks were falling around us. For me, a person who gets dizzy on high heels, the feeling of height was just awful. I wanted to close my eyes, because no matter how carefully I chose my steps I couldn't help glancing down at that smoldering fuel truck.

The water well drillers came to our rescue from camp. We assumed they must have got in before the road gave way. They told us that the driver of the fuel truck had burned with his cargo. That dreadful piece of information shook us all up. My brother made his living servicing rigs and drove a fuel truck nearly every day of his life. I knew there was no chance of my brother being in that area, but the whole situation made all of us very nervous.

The camp crew – my helper, the camp attendant and myself – had been sent in to prepare camp for the arrival of more rig hands who would arrive as soon as the road was passable. Three of the crew were already in camp. They had been sent in to "camp watch" and to start setting up the trailers. They had the power plant in operation, but none of the hallways, floors or roofs were in place. It was a sad looking camp when I saw it for the first time. Some of the dirt was still clinging to the side of the cookhouse, where it had obviously turned over during the move. There was mud everywhere. Somehow, I had hoped that the mountains and British Columbia would relieve us of mud, but I was wrong. I've been told there is no escape from mud on a drilling rig — unless one goes to the deserts of Iran.

To make matters worse, we woke up to find grizzly bear tracks all around camp. I ranted and raved about these tracks and demanded the protection of at least one sharpshooter. In most camps, the rig is quite a distance from camp, and during the daytime, when the day shift is out working, the night shift is sleeping. With the constant noise from the power plant, a cook could yell her head off and not rouse those rig hands. The thought of one of those huge creatures breaking into camp terrified me.

After a lot of patting on the shoulder and pacifying words like, "Don't worry Bev, those bears will be long gone as soon as we start drilling," I still wasn't convinced. I continued to bellyache, and finally the push put my old friend Alvin, who was an excellent shot, on night-shift so he would be in camp during the day. I sweet-talked the campy into moving Alvin right next to the rec trailer, so that he would be closer to the kitchen and our quarters. I was right in his room when he checked his rifle to make sure it was loaded. Even so, I spent a lot of time going backwards to make sure a bear wasn't following me when I went from the kitchen down the hallway or out to the garbage. One day the campy and I went out to measure the footprints. They were about eight inches in diameter. That is a large bear!

We didn't actually see a bear during our first week in camp, but they were coming around. We saw tracks after every snowfall. I took to sleeping with my clothes on, so I could make a quick exit if the bears tried to break into camp. I was sure it would be through my quarters. I was quickly becoming a nervous wreck.

To add to my terror, every time anyone arrived from the Cat camp, where the road construction crew stayed, they would spin stories about the terrible flights into the area. The pilot was making waves about not being able to take off with a full load. He said he needed a longer strip, but everyone had an excuse as to why no Cat or dozer was available. I think it was because there weren't enough bulldozers and cats in the valley yet; they were still out building an access road for the rig loads.

This may not sound very dangerous, but when you have flown in small plane for as many miles as I have, often without proper landing strips, it's quite terrifying. I was afraid to ask too many questions and concentrated on my bear problem. As my long change came nearer, I wasn't able to sleep at all. I was torn between staying in that valley and being eaten by grizzly bears or boarding that little plane and crashing because the strip wasn't long enough. When the great day finally arrived, I opted for the plane crash. I had to get out of Grizzly Valley.

Shortly after breakfast, we all piled into trucks to drive the fifteen miles to the Cat camp. When we arrived, the engineer told us the plane would be a little late. We dug into the cook's pastry display and drank coffee for the next two hours.

A glance at the pastry table told me we must have consumed at least thirty pounds of food. This did not sit too well with me, as we had all been told to keep our weight down to the bare minimum. I realized this meant our gear, but my overactive imagination suggested to me that the extra body weight just might cause the plane to crash.

We heard the drone of the engine and made a mad dash to the strip to see the little plane come out of the clouds and circle the area. I silently watched it land. It took every inch of the landing strip. The pilot taxied up to where we were gathered. As he went by I could see my relief cook in the front seat; her face was as white as a sheet. Then I saw the wire holding the door shut!

I watched the five incoming crew members climb out of the plane and open the freight doors on the wing compartments. I couldn't believe that little plane could carry that mountain of cargo, and our crew had two more people than the one that was getting off!

When the woman stepped down, I saw why the door had been wired shut. She was nearly as broad as she was tall. I heard, much later, that the laughter over wiring the door shut had soon turned into fright. The trip had been extremely rough.

There was no bantering between the incoming and outgoing crews that day. The relief push grabbed his gear and headed for the trucks. I heard him say to a cat skinner who was watching the whole operation, "I sure as hell am glad to set foot on terra firma. Never thought we'd

make it. Worst flight I ever took." Dear God! And I had
to board that plane if I was ever going to get out of
Grizzly Valley.

The outgoing crew began stuffing, shoving and
pushing our gear into the compartments. I flung my bag
over to them and watched. Any fool could see we had
twice as much gear as the crew which had just arrived.
And all those pastries too.

The pilot motioned for me to board and pointed to
the front seat. As I was the only woman in that crew, I
suppose he thought it only polite, but I yelled something
about sitting further back. I had read somewhere it was
safer than in the front. I struggled aboard, fastened my
safety belt and began to pray. I watched the crew drive
off on their journey to the rig and prayed none of them
would be eaten by the bears in my absence. What was I
praying about anyway? Surely I wasn't coming back into
this God-forsaken country, was I? My prayer got all
mixed up at that point.

The pilot turned the plane around to take full
advantage of the thirty or so feet of strip behind us. He
revved up, or whatever it is that a pilot does when his
engines start to whine, and we were off down the strip at
full speed. Even in my demented state, I was sure we
couldn't take off. I gripped the arm rest so hard that my
knuckles went white. We piled into the snow bank at the
end of the strip. The snow was soft, so we didn't feel the
bump too badly, although my neck was jerked, and I saw
stars for a few minutes.

The pilot's head appeared around the curtain, and
asked for some help shovelling snow. Everyone got out
of the plane except me. I knew that if I ever got out I

would never get back in again. I could see the cat skinner running over with a bunch of snow shovels. It took less than ten minutes and we were back at the starting point again. The rig hands all ran back with their shovels over their shoulders. I was quite relieved to see them running, as I was sure they would burn off a few of those pastry pounds.

When the plane arrived back at the camp end of the strip, the pilot suggested that everyone shovel a few more feet at that end of the strip before putting the shovels away. That took about another 15 minutes. Then we were off down the strip full speed ahead for the second time. We didn't make it that time either. By then I was almost hysterical. I was too far gone to notice that some of the others were just as scared as me.

When we hit the snow bank the second time, I was sure the pilot didn't know what he was doing. I should have known he was too young to have any experience, but he seemed calm and not in the least bit upset over our predicament. He yelled that we'd make it on the third try for sure and pointed to the cat camp where we could see the skinner approaching the strip with a blade on a truck.

The pilot turned the plane around, and we taxied back down to where the skinner was running the blade right up to the brush at the end of the strip. It would give us another fifty feet or so. When he waved to the pilot, we taxied to the very end of the newly ploughed strip, and we were off again. We became airborne, but I swear we chopped off whole chunks of tree tops when we left the strip. To this day I do not know why they didn't plough the strip out properly before we ever attempted to take off.

During all the commotion and fright I had forgotten to pray, so I took it up again even more seriously. We kept falling into air pockets and finally the pilot stuck his head around the curtain again to tell us we were experiencing turbulence and not to worry. When the pilot kept repeating himself about this turbulence, I began to worry about him. Surely to God something was wrong. It was even more bumpy than riding in a truck on a rig road. I opened my eyes to look around at my fellow passengers. Three of them were using those little brown bags that are on all planes. I closed my eyes again and thanked my lucky stars I didn't get airsick — only airscared.

As soon as we were out of the foothills, the plane straightened out and we had a smooth flight into the city of Grand Prairie, where our cold trucks were lined up beside the airport terminal. As I was waiting for my truck to warm up, I silently promised myself I would never go back into Grizzly Valley. I couldn't put myself through that again. Could I?

My entire week out was spent pacing the floor trying to decide what to do. I was torn between my horrible fear of flying, my fear of bears, and the terrible isolation of that place, and the good pay cheque I earned for my efforts. My nights were filled with dreams of horror. I'd see myself mauled by grizzlies or mangled in plane crashes. Then I'd see images of my funeral, and I'd wake up sweating or crying. I had to quit! I couldn't go back! But I did.

When I arrived at the airport a week later, I had to wait for the plane to make an emergency trip into the valley with parts for another rig. Because of the weight, he couldn't take me or our groceries and supplies. I sat for an additional two hours dreaming up all kinds of accidents and encounters with huge grizzly bears. I watched the nice, friendly white clouds turn to a dark blue and knew it would be snowing and windy in the pass. As darkness settled in, I secretly prayed that the pilot didn't have his instrument rating, needed to fly at night, and that we would have to wait until daylight. In my panic, I thought that if I was going to meet my Maker, I would like it to be in the daylight so that I could see how I was going to get there.

No such luck. Those pilots flew twenty-four hours a day. I had to get on that plane even though it was pitch black. I was the sole passenger, so the pilot asked me if I wanted to sit up front. I accepted. What the heck. While I strapped myself in, I saw him fooling around with his panel and heard him talking to the tower. Then we were off down the paved strip, smooth as silk. And then we were airborne. I watched the lights of the city fade as we approached the foothills, and then it dawned on me: the landing strip at the cat camp didn't have lights. How were we going to land? I thought I should pass on this piece of information as quickly as possible.

"That strip at the cat camp doesn't have any lights. How are we going to land?"

"It does now. They put lights in on Friday. I had to make an emergency flight in. Had to bring a guy out . . . mauled by a grizzly." He just kept right on flying.

Now, wasn't that cute. Mauled by a grizzly! "Where?" I asked.

"The guy was working on one of those rigs in the Valley. Don't know which one. Couldn't have been too far from where you're going. I picked him up at that strip."

Sure. He didn't have to worry. He could fly back to civilization. He wasn't stuck out here among the grizzly bears. I didn't say much for the remainder of the trip. I had visions of a newspaper headline. "COOK KILLED IN PLANE CRASH AFTER BEING MAULED BY GRIZZLY."

Oh God! If I had had a bottle of anything, I think I would have drank it all.

Then we hit turbulence again. Turbulence is one of the most hated words in my vocabulary. Even when flying on a commercial plane, I hate to hear that word. The flight was terrible, but we did land in one piece, and I stepped down on terra firma vowing to give up this lifestyle as soon as I possibly could. I was making more rash promises to myself.

My whole tour of duty in that valley was a nightmare. Grizzly bears and plane rides. Each trip in and out was worse than the previous one. If I wasn't worrying about one, I was worrying about the other. After the second trip into camp we still weren't spudded in, or drilling. Everything that could go wrong went wrong on that rig. I had been assured that as soon as we began drilling the bears would leave. Every time anyone came into camp from the rig site, I would ask if they were drilling yet. I made such a fuss the push finally realized just how bad off I really was. I asked him several times to find a replacement for me, or to ask the office people to send me anywhere else. He kept telling me we would be just fine as soon as we got down to steady drilling. I think he did ask to have me sent elsewhere, but I'm sure it wasn't to another rig.

To keep me satisfied, the push brought his rifle in and set it by the kitchen door. He knew I could handle a rifle, but I know I would probably have panicked if a bear broke into camp. I continued to look behind me a lot and became more nervous and panicky every day. Some of the real fast runners in camp took to sneaking up on me and then shouting "BOO" just to see me jump, release a scream of terror, and go running down the hall.

Finally the bears left as predicted but, sure enough, after a week, we found more tracks very close to camp again. Without telling anyone except me, Alvin went out looking for the bear. He said he'd found a carcass the bear was feeding on and some tracks that were so fresh the water was still running into them. He thought that was about as far as he was going to go in tracking that bear. Even Alvin, who was part native and an excellent shot, and who had hunted most of his life, was not taking any chances with the grizzlies in Grizzly Valley.

Every time anyone drove into camp, he had another bear story. As these stories increased so did my terror. After the second mauling in the pass, our push instructed us to keep our hallways clear of meats and pastries, as we often used the hallway as a cooler. Our camp had been secured with heavy doors on each end of the hallways, but it wasn't grizzly-proof by any means.

And then it happened! A bear broke into camp.

My helper and I were sleeping. It was during our afternoon rest period, and, with the constant noise from the motors, we didn't hear a thing. Our campy heard a commotion, peered out of his door, and saw the bear. He quickly closed the door and didn't hear the bear as it passed his doorway dragging a bag of garbage. He was too busy trying to get his window open for an escape route. After several attempts, he knew it was useless — the window was frozen shut. He started to yell at the top of his lungs and woke a sleeping rig hand. The campy kept yelling there was a bear in camp, but the sleepy rig hand walked down the hallway to the campy's room anyway. He didn't see the bear at the other end of the hallway.

The only other rig hand who had a rifle was awakened by the ruckus and came out into the hallway with his rifle loaded and ready to fire. He just saw the tail end of the bear as it left through the broken doorway. He didn't fire his gun. Alvin then backed out of the opposite hallway to a service truck parked in front of camp and drove out to the rig to get permission to hunt the bear down. He got it. One other rig hand went with Alvin and they were back in camp within an hour. They had shot the bear.

I think every man in camp went along to bring the bear in. No one had a licence, and it was against government regulations to shoot a grizzly, so we kept it pretty much quiet, but the story did leak out eventually. We had no scales to weigh the bear, but an intelligent estimate would have put it around 700 pounds. By the time the camp moved, the story had gotten taller. The bear weighed over a ton, was shot right in camp and had mauled half the crew before it was shot down.

I couldn't believe I slept through the whole thing. I thought they were kidding when they told me Alvin had gone out to hunt down the bear. It was no joke. That bear was for real.

My nightmares became horrors of great huge bears clawing at my window or door. I was even worse after the bear was shot. I was sure there was another bear waiting to break into camp. I don't remember too much else besides bears and the dreadful flights into that valley, but eventually we did move out.

Some people might question my sanity at staying on any job that frightened me so badly, but I wasn't scared of bears all the time — just nearly all the time. When we went into those isolated camps, we knew there would be bears. It was a matter of trying to overcome that terror. Nowhere else was I and, a lot of other women, able to make so much money, and most of the time it was fun. I enjoyed cooking so much. It never seemed like hard work, except when we were moving a rig camp. It was the first, and only, time in my life that I had absolutely everything I needed, or wanted, to cook with. Most days, I enjoyed producing good hearty meals. Men who work outdoors in cold temperatures consume a lot of food just to keep warm. Good, attractive meals were important in a camp; supper time was the event of the day. I used to threaten the guys when they teased and made jokes about bears. I told them that I would go on strike and not bake bread any more. What a catastrophe that would be!

Many of us were afraid of bears, but if one used some intelligence and didn't go into the bush alone, it was relatively safe. Only occasionally did a bear break into a camp. Wildlife people tell us there will be more encounters with these creatures as the drilling continues in isolated areas. We are the intruders, not the bears.

Chapter Five

Bear Attacks

SHORTLY BEFORE I LEFT the rigs for good, two people lost their lives in the Zama area of northern Alberta, where a Cantex drilling rig was in operation. The incident occurred about twenty-five miles from that tiny village.

It was in August of 1980 when a geologist, Lee Randal Morris, who was assigned to the Cantex rig, went for a walk one evening and was attacked by a bear. Morris, who was unarmed, was mauled and killed. The body was dragged to a spot where it was partially eaten. The bear was in the process of burying his kill when two others from the same camp, a man and a woman, took the same route for their evening walk. The two, twenty-four year-old Carol Ann Marshall and 20 year-old Marty Ellis, were also charged by the bear. They attempted to climb two nearby trees. Ellis was trying to help Carol, but she lost her hold and the bear got her. He bit into her neck and shook her. Ellis later told police, who were investigating the killing, that he was sure Carol was killed instantly. The bear then dragged Carol's body off into the bush, where she too, was partially eaten and buried.

But that didn't satisfy the bear. He came back after Ellis who was about twenty feet up the tree. The bear climbed up after Ellis who kept kicking the bear's head while he climbed higher. Ellis said he kicked at the bear several times trying to knock it out of the tree, but it refused to budge for a long time.

Ellis, at this point, was still unaware that the bear had killed the geologist. When the bear had returned from dragging Carol's body away, Ellis saw a boy, the twelve year-old son of the consulting engineer on the rig, walking down the path that he and Carol had walked on earlier. Ellis shouted at the boy to run back and get his father and a gun.

At first, because of the noise from the rig, the boy didn't hear Ellis' screams for help. He just kept coming, but finally he did hear Ellis' shouts. The boy then ran back to the rig to get his father. When he told the senior Whiting that Ellis was fighting off a bear, the engineer armed himself with a .300 Winchester magnum rifle and left for the scene.

When he approached the tree with Ellis still clinging to the uppermost branches, the bear charged Whiting who then shot it three times. The bear rolled over, got up and went back into the bush. Whiting did not know how badly the bear was wounded, but Ellis came down out of the tree and the three hurried back to camp. The RCMP were notified by mobile phone, and other Cantex rig workers went out in search of the two missing people. They found their remains and brought the bodies into camp. By that time it was dark, but the next day, a wildlife crew was sent out by helicopter to locate and shoot the bear. When the bear's carcass was sent to

Edmonton, it proved to be the right bear. Its stomach contents included some jean material and pieces of Morris' shirt.

It was a terrible tragedy. When I read about it, I didn't feel too foolish about my terror of bears. Not one of those people was armed, and they were in no way antagonizing the bear. They just happened to be in its territory at the wrong time. That was the chance we all took.

Chapter Six

Idiosyncrasies

RIG HANDS, LIKE EVERYONE ELSE in the world, have idiosyncrasies. The longer they stay out in the bush, the more likely these small quirks are going to show up and aggravate everyone around them. Living in close quarters can be difficult if you let these things get to you. To make the stay as pleasant as possible, one learns to accept them. Let me tell you about a couple of the characters that I met along the black gold trail.

Mike, one of my favourite engineers, just hated to leave the rig. I worked with him on several jobs and still didn't know anything about him. I don't think anyone else knew much about Mike either. He was one of a kind, that guy!

When he arrived in camp it was for the duration of the drilling on that well. His only excursions into town were few, and necessary — like when his head office requested he use a land phone to make his report or when he needed a haircut.

Mike was extremely shy and was ill at ease around women and newcomers. When I first met him I thought he was very rednecked, but after I got to know him, I put it down to being old-fashioned. They threw away the mold when they made guys like Mike.

He arrived in camp one afternoon and announced his name and occupation: "I'm Mike. Been over at 31 . . . back in the bush there. I'm gonna be the overseer on this job here . . . if you can put up with me that long."

Mike liked to see a nice, clean camp with women in the kitchen. Indeed, Mike thought all women should be in the kitchen and nowhere else.

He told our push he'd been on his last job for nearly six months, and by the look of his hair, I don't think he got anywhere near a barber in that time. He was desperately in need of a haircut.

Keeping one's hair trimmed is mandatory on the rigs, but Mike went only by Mike's rules. He was very good at his job, and he, his head office - and everyone else who ever worked with him - knew it.

Rig workers are required by law to wear face masks when they are drilling through sour gas. A face mask won't fit properly if there is too much facial or head hair. The rules are supposed to be enforced by the tool pusher. If, by any chance, the push is negligent in this respect, the oil company representatives, the engineer or geologist will enforce them — hence the necessity for Mike to get a haircut as soon as possible.

The tool push at the time was a pretty good guy, but he was quite young and he had a young crew. He had the respect of all his men, but he was a bit lax when it came to regulations — especially those relating to hair cuts. Mike could see at one glance around the supper table that this rule had to be enforced, but he couldn't very well do it until his own hair was cut. We all knew they were drilling in a sour gas field.

Mike had replaced an engineer who had been sent overseas. He was planning to stay until we had completed the well, as we were almost finished drilling when he arrived. From the first day on the job, his reports had to be made on a land phone. On that first day, he told my helper and I that he would be going into Fox Creek after lunch to make his report, and he offered to pick up anything we might need. My helper and I were quite surprised to hear this thoughtful offer, but I guess that was his way of saying he may be late for supper and to please save it for him. With roads as unpredictable as they were in that area, no one knew just when they would return from a trip to town.

We all thought Mike was going to get a haircut as well as use the land phone. He arrived back at camp right on schedule for supper, but he still didn't have a haircut. Within a few minutes of his return, this news ran right through the camp gossip mill.

Right after Mike had left that morning, I had promised the entire day shift I would cut their hair right after their shift was over. They weren't taking any chances with Mike on the scene. Even the tool pusher made an appointment to get his hair cut, right after the roughnecks. No one said a word about Mike not getting his hair cut.

I started the haircuts as soon as supper was over. Two roughnecks were sent into the kitchen to do the dishes for us. After I finished the first "customer," Mike appeared in the doorway of the rec trailer. I nodded to Mike and kept on cutting. I noticed him leave, but he returned with a cup of coffee and a newspaper. I glanced over at him several times and knew he wasn't reading; he was watching what I was doing. He replenished his coffee several times, and on each trip he walked around the roughneck to make a careful examination of my handiwork. He was still there drinking coffee and "reading" his newspaper when the push sat down for his haircut. After each roughneck was finished with their cut they went to the washroom to get a better look. I noticed Mike followed each man. I suspect it was to get a better view under the bright lights in the washroom.

When I was all finished for the evening, Mike followed me down the hallway. Just as I was about to enter my quarters he smiled and started examining the floor between us. "Uh . . . say there, Bev. I . . . uh . . . wondered if you might just give me a little trim, if you've got enough time, of course."

"Sure, Mike. How about first thing in the morning . . . after breakfast. Is that OK?"

"Fine, fine. Anytime it's convenient with you." With that he started down the hallway to the kitchen. He suddenly turned around and said, "Say there, Bev. Did you know they've got a lady barber in Fox Creek?"

"Yes, I heard that. Heard she's pretty good too," I said.

"Never know where you might find a woman these days!" Mike turned away and hurried out of sight.

Poor Mike. So that was why he didn't get his hair cut in Fox Creek. For a minute there, I wondered what Mike thought I was. But for some reason I understood. Mike just couldn't face the fact that there were women in what he considered a man's bastion: a barber shop.

The next day I cut Mike's hair. As soon as it was respectable, he darted down the hallway to the men's washroom to examine my work. He returned to thank me profusely and said, "I'll get a little something for you next time I'm in town."

By lunch time I'd heard, via the rig grapevine, that Mike had taken quite a teasing from his peers about, "Just what were you and the cook doing in there for such a long time?" Rig hands said he was as scarce as hen's teeth all afternoon. For the next week, Mike blushed every time he entered the dining room.

A few days after his haircut, Mike showed up at the kitchen doorway and asked my helper and me to come down to the push's office, if we could spare the time.

Poor old Mike. He was too shy to present me with a gift without the support of another man. He was pacing the floor when we arrived. He asked us to have a little "smash" with him and the push. I was shocked at his version of a little smash. I took one look at the tumbler half filled with amber liquid and said, "No thanks, Mike. We're still on duty." The push nodded at me, so I accepted out of courtesy. My helper did likewise.

After fussing around for several minutes, Mike finally picked up a shopping bag and shoved it toward me. "Sure appreciate you cutting my hair, Bev. There's a little something in there for both of you." His face was so red, he couldn't look at either of us. All of a sudden, Mike was greatly interested in the linoleum on the office floor.

My helper and I dug into the bag and it was like Christmas. There were at least a dozen good magazines, three day-old newspapers, which are precious on a rig camp, two huge boxes of expensive chocolates, two cartons of my brand of cigarettes, and a bottle of the finest rye whisky I ever drank. I couldn't believe my eyes. All this for cutting Mike's hair!

The push grabbed one of the papers, my helper another and we cracked open a box of chocolates. We were so busy we didn't notice Mike leave the room. I took the last newspaper and went back into the dining room where I held it up for grabs. Everyone in the room grabbed a piece of it and argued over who had the front page. Mike sat in a corner eating his supper, watching everything that was going on.

It's hard to believe there are men as shy as Mike was. He continued to bring newspapers back to camp every time he was in town, and I continued to cut his hair at two different holes after that. He always rewarded me with about three times what an ordinary haircut would cost him in town, but Mike wasn't about to be caught in a barber shop where there was a woman barber, no sir-ee.

I worked with another character, an older tool push, who had false teeth and just couldn't get used to them. When I first met him, he didn't have them in and he apologized by saying, "Sorry I haven't got my teeth in right now. Got some store bought ones . . . and having a bad time getting used to them." I think I heard him say that line a hundred times or more.

That push would always run out to the rig first thing every morning. When he returned he would come into the dining room and sit down for breakfast. As soon as he took a mouthful of food, he would remember he didn't have his teeth in, and he'd make a quick dash into his office. When he came back into the room he would make some sort of comment about getting used to his "new" teeth. If we had new rig hands, or visitors, he would always make the same comment. All of us would glance at one another, but there was no snickering or snide remarks. We respected that push too much to make fun of him. We just went along with his story about his "new" teeth.

Chapter Seven

Injury

EVERY LITTLE PAIN SEEMS WORSE when one is a long way from civilization and a doctor. A toothache for example, can draw sympathy from everyone in camp for a while. After the immediate sympathy has worn off, the constant belly-aching becomes a real pain to those who have to listen to it.

When someone did have a toothache, we would all scout around in our own gear for medication. It has always been a wonder to me why drilling companies don't include toothache drops in their first-aid kit, because that seems to be the most common source of pain, apart from accidents, among young people who are otherwise healthy and fit.

If we were unable to locate any medication for a toothache, then it was back to the spice rack. My father used to pack our cavities with nutmeg, and more than once I used this treatment on rig hands. It isn't the treatment so much that helps, it's the sympathy and attention that goes along with it. If everyone coming into camp doesn't ask how the poor soul is who's suffering from this dreaded malady, then that person is deeply hurt.

If, however, they do ask how that person is, and if the toothache is better, then all is well. The person recovering from his toothache will enter into a very long and detailed monologue on how the toothache started, why it will continue to cause so much pain and what type of treatment is being done, and by whom. If the listener is still interested, he will then go on to tell, in detail, what measures will be taken in the future to prevent the same thing from happening again.

I knew a rig hand who was continually complaining about a toothache. After treating him several times with appropriate spices and a swallow or two of my precious brandy, I would politely listen to his long list of excuses as to why he didn't have it pulled or filled on his last week out.

This same rig hand was horribly mangled when his hand got caught in the chain and tongs on the rig platform while his crew was tripping.

The push brought him into camp and asked me to look after him while he mobiled for a chopper to take him out to a hospital. Like most rig hands, I'd taken a first aid course, but it didn't prepare me for that mangled hand. It was a mass of exposed flesh. There was surprisingly very little blood. I fought back tears and the terrible sense of wanting to faint. Two fingers were missing entirely, and his thumb was barely attached to his hand. When I looked at his hand I forgot everything I ever learned about first aid. I kept busy so that he wouldn't be frightened.

When I got the grease and oil washed off the rest of his hand I got up enough courage to look at the roughneck. There were beads of perspiration on his face, which was terribly white. I could see the pain in his eyes, but he hadn't uttered a single word. He just kept watching what I was doing. I sent my helper to my room to get the brandy and poured a shot for him. He gratefully accepted it and downed it in one gulp. Then we heard the chopper.

He walked out of that camp and climbed into the machine without any help from the many of us who stood there watching and waving to him. He still hadn't uttered a word, but we knew he was in terrible pain.

I went back into camp and sat down at the table. My knees wouldn't hold me any longer. Then I started laughing. The push came in and sat down opposite me. He poured a coffee and slid it across the table toward me. When I didn't respond he came around and patted me on the shoulder. I stopped laughing and began to cry. Crying was something the push could handle. He knew it was a reaction from seeing the most mangled hand he or I had ever seen. We sat there drinking coffee until I got control of myself again.

The push broke the silence. "Remember when he had that toothache? You'd have thought he was dying. Complained to everyone in camp about it didn't he?" The push was thinking along the same lines I was. "And now, when he really had something to complain about, he never said a word."

After some miracle surgery performed by doctors in Edmonton, that roughneck recovered the use of his thumb, and he went on with his career in the oil patch. The last time I saw him he was drilling but had lost two more fingers in subsequent accidents.

Missing fingers and toes are not uncommon in the oil patch. I know one driller who has a total of two fingers and one thumb. His only comment is that he's sure glad to have one thumb so that he can hold the drilling stick while on duty and a glass when he's off.

Some rig hands are so shy or embarrassed, they don't want to talk about their accidents. Others will tell you every detail whether you want to hear it or not. They will go on about how it happened and where it occurred. If you're still listening after that, you can hear the details about the rig hand's stay in hospital, including a full description of every nurse, and most of his life story since losing that finger or toe.

When two old rig hands get together who have experienced the same dilemma, they will clamour for rights to tell their story first. Spectator attention to these long stories is determined by the pecking order of the rig hand telling it. If he is a driller, then all his crew will marvel at every word. If he is a roughneck, then he will find himself blubbering away to the walls before the story is finished. It all boils down to respect. If the crew respects a person they will grant him listening time. If they don't like him, someone will tell him to shut up and let someone else talk. Respect must be earned.

Chapter Eight

Power Failure

ANOTHER CANDLELIT DINNER. Three nights in a row. It was unacceptable. Who ever heard of this happening on a rig camp anyway? It's not that I didn't enjoy a dinner by candlelight once in a while . . . but out here in the bush . . . with 35 rig hands for company?

I was sitting in front of the kitchen, my feet in the oven, watching the evening set in. It was in the latter part of November: the year Mr. Joe Clark was ousted from his prime ministership. Mr. Clark was not the only Albertan who was suffering from humiliation and chilly responses from his peers. Perry, our motorman on the day shift was running neck and neck with him. Perry could not get the power plant at camp to keep running.

I was cold and tired. I couldn't sleep because my quarters were as cold as an iceberg. I marvelled at how my helper Carol managed to keep warm enough to sleep. I contemplated waking her, as it was nearly 4:30 p.m. and we had supper to get ready, but I thought I might as well let her rest.

Being without power in a camp wasn't unusual, but this was a major problem. For the last five days it had been off and on all day — sometimes for two hour stretches. A camp can get awfully cold in two hours. Because of the power problem, we had done most of the meal preparations during daylight hours.

I slipped my jacket around my shoulders and wondered if, by any chance, my truck would start. Like all the vehicles in camp, it had been sitting for nearly ten days since we had pulled onto the new lease. They were plugged in, but with such undependable power, it was unlikely that any of them would start.

This last rig and camp move had been a disaster. The kitchen had turned over en route. The truck driver, who had been moving it, had lost his way in the parking lot of the hotel in Fox Creek and had ended up at another lease. In his haste to find the proper lease, he had gone too fast on the treacherous curves.

The camp was old and the rig had been rebuilt. Some of our more experienced rig hands said that the motors must have come over on the ark. They cursed the previous motormen and head office when they were cold and couldn't see down the hall. It was especially frustrating, because every man in camp knew there were new motors sitting at head office in Nisku. For some reason they had never been sent.

The first tool push had been replaced shortly after the move. Our old friend Woody had been recalled, again, to help out in an emergency. It was my opinion that if old Woody couldn't keep the motors running they were worn out. Good old Woody. He was the tooly who bragged that he could mend anything from a broken heart to the crack of dawn, but he just couldn't keep those motors running.

The slam of a door brought me out of my daydreaming. Carol entered the kitchen with a blanket wrapped around her over top of her jacket. She was shivering from the cold. She grabbed a chair, sat down in front of the stove, and shoved her feet into the oven alongside mine. She didn't have much to say.

"I'm going out to see if my truck will start," I said. " If it does, I'm leaving. Wanna come along?"

"Yes, of course I will," she said. "This is ridiculous, it's a wonder we all haven't got pneumonia by now."

"If it won't go, I'll just run down to the rig and get Perry," I said. "We've got to have power for supper." I slipped into my boots and left the warm kitchen. It was the only place in camp that was warm.

I got snow down my neck when I opened my truck door. That got me cursing even before I found out that my truck wouldn't start. Not once did that motor turn over. I gave up in disgust. I didn't want to wear my battery out. I slammed the door shut and got another shower of snow down the front of my jacket. I was just starting up the trail to the rig site, when I saw Woody's truck coming. I kicked a bit of snow back into the tracks leading to my truck in the hopes that he wouldn't notice what I had been up to. He was such a nice guy that I hated to run off on him, but this past ten days had been a nightmare. Any sane woman would have left camp long ago. I went back into the kitchen.

We heard his truck pull up in front of camp, but he didn't come in. Soon we heard him out at the power plant. In a few minutes we heard the motor start up and then a dim glow spread over the room. A few more turns and we had power again. Carol and I scampered around camp to light the furnaces in the various rooms down the hall. We heard Woody go into his office and get on the mobile phone. Neither of us were very interested in what he was saying, so we retired to our warm kitchen.

I took a roast out of the second oven and began making gravy. Carol was fighting with the dishrag that kept freezing to the table when she tried to wipe it. We heard the push when he left for the rig. I knew he must have seen my tracks where I'd gone out to my truck. That old boy wasn't stupid. He knew I was fed up and on the verge of leaving camp. However, he was also pretty sure I wouldn't leave camp at this time of day even if my truck had started.

He was a worried man. He had inherited a can of worms when he was given the job of setting up this rig and camp. Most pushes would have been deserted by this time, with conditions so bad, but everyone liked Woody and stuck around just because of that.

We continued supper preparations chatting about leaving if, or when, we could get my truck going. We decided to wait it out and see what the rig hands would do. It was a bit foolish for two women to set out on a 33-mile drive on a rig road — this late at night, anyway. If we did leave, it would have to be early in the day.

The men on the night shift drifted into the kitchen. From the look of them, they must have slept in their clothes after coming off shift the night before. It was so cold in camp, it was a wonder any of them slept that long. They were all about as owly as I was. A few snarls were exchanged.

The motorman on shift was cursed, and five large men tried to get all ten feet into the oven at the same time. It wasn't exactly pleasant trying to get a meal ready with all this going on. I advised them that they might get scalded or burnt, but it wasn't enough to get any of them to move. I informed them that there was hot water in one of those large pots on the grill if they wanted to wash up but to be careful — one had soup in it. It was so dark in that kitchen we couldn't tell soup from water. The driller got up and poured a half potful into the kitchen sink and washed right there. His crew followed suit. We didn't complain. By then I couldn't have cared less where anyone washed or what anyone did.

When Carol called the men to the table, ten feet disappeared like magic. The roughneck from the day shift came in the back door for his rig box and stuck his feet in the oven while we dished up. "Roast beef?" he asked. It was all the conversation he could muster at the time. He left without another word.

When the first crew was finished eating, we wondered why the "elite" crew hadn't arrived. They were usually the first to arrive for any meal. We decided there must be unexpected problems at the rig, so we dished out our meal and sat down to eat. As soon as we did, twelve men walked in and headed to the kitchen to dish up their plates. We didn't get up to wait on them, and we didn't speak to any of them. Just as Woody sat down, the power gave out again. I reached for my lighter and lit the ever-ready candle at my end of the table. Soon, there were candles going on every table. Woody went to his office and got a flashlight and set it upside down at the end of his table. We all finished our meal in silence.

As soon as Woody was finished eating, he nodded at the driller, and they went out the back door to the power plant. We could hear them shouting and cursing but the thing refused to start. They were still out there trying to coax it into operation two hours later.

Carol and I cleaned up the dishes, tidied up the kitchen as best we could under candle light, and sat down with our feet in the oven again. We waited, and waited, and waited. Nothing happened. It just kept getting colder. The night shift came back into the kitchen to warm their feet before they left for their twelve hours on duty. There was none of the usual banter and teasing that went on when things were going well. It was a very depressing situation. They left without a word.

Half an hour later we heard the day shift hit camp. Not one of them went to their rooms. They headed straight for the only warm spot in camp: the kitchen. In a few minutes there were boots and gloves scattered all over the kitchen floor. More chairs were brought in and five more men tried, unsuccessfully, to put their feet in the oven beside ours. We refused to move. I pointed to the second oven and they nearly fell off their chairs fighting for positions in front of it. One foolish roughneck went into the dining room to pour himself a cup of coffee from the urn that was always plugged in. He came back with, "How come the coffee's cold in there, Bev?"

That brought a barrage of laughter. "Why do you think it's cold?" said one of the men. The "roughy" realized his error immediately and sat down and shut up. It wasn't for long. "Couldn't you make some coffee on the stove Bev?" he asked.

"Why don't you make coffee on the stove if you want some?" Carol asked. The roughy began opening every cupboard in an effort to locate coffee. I got up in disgust and measured out coffee into an old pot. I reached for the kettle which was singing on the back of the grill. Because of the poor light, I poured boiling water over my hand. I jumped back, knocked two or three rig hands off their chairs, and let out a bellow of curse words that would have startled the most hardened rig hand. A burn was just what I needed about then. I left the room and headed across the hall to nurse my wound. When I returned nearly every rig hand offered their chair and the choice spot in front of the stove. I was not in a good mood. Even the grumbling stopped. They drank their coffee in silence.

As I sat there feeling sorry for myself, I watched in horror as the flame under the pot slowly went out. Price, the driller, looked at me and shook his head.

"I don't believe it," he said. "We can't be out of propane. At least I don't think we can. Probably frozen lines." He pushed the derrickman off his chair, and they both left to see what had caused the propane to go out. I don't think any of the others knew what had happened. A few minutes later the roughneck said,

"How come you turned the coffee off, Bev?" There seemed no end to this roughy's stupid remarks.

"Because we're either out of propane or the lines are frozen," I said as I glared at him again. "Why don't you go out and help Price see what's wrong?" It was the only way I could think of to get rid of him. He, of course, left. His curiosity was astounding.

Carol went to our room to get blankets. We covered up and sat by the oven which was slowly growing cold. The grill would keep us warm for some time, but when that lost its heat it wouldn't be very comfortable in camp. The propane stove was the only source of heat when the power failed. Somebody had to do something pretty darn fast. We heard Price come into the hallway and go out again. He came into the kitchen with a grim look on his face.

"My truck won't start either, Bev," he said. Woody must have told him that I'd tried my truck earlier.

"The propane lines are frozen," he said. "It'll take some time to get them thawed out. I'm gonna go down and talk to Woody to see what we should do. And what about you girls? Getting a bit fed up eh, Bev?"

"We gotta do something pretty darn fast here now. It's gonna take awhile to get those lines thawed out and ... we still don't know how much propane's in that tank. Can't see the dial and Mel kept terrible records." Price was frowning as he dug around in his tool kit.

We heard Woody's truck drive up and then more loud shouting from the power plant. Then the power came on again. It flickered and died. The men came in from the plant and held a meeting in front of the grill. Just when they were about to send us all into town, the power came on again. It was beyond a joke. We all knew it wouldn't stay on for any length of time. It was obvious we couldn't stay in camp.

Woody and Price went down the hall to Woody's office. The rest of us growled and snarled at each other. I could hear Woody talking to head office on the mobile again, and then he came into the kitchen. Price was right behind him.

"You girls wanna go for a drive?" asked Woody. The prospect of a drive didn't really move us. "I'm expecting an electrician," he said. "Shoulda been here this morning. He's probably in a snow bank along the road. I've gotta go get him." He went to the grill and poured coffee into a thermos. He grinned at me as he put the lid on it.

"Got something I'm gonna mix with this," he said. "It'll warm you girls up on the road." He waited for us to grab our boots and we were off. The thought of a nice warm truck was just too much for us. Got sucked in again.

We drove down the trail at a steady twenty miles an hour watching on both sides of the road. There was bright moonlight, and it would have been a beautiful evening if wasn't so cold and we weren't in such a sour mood. Woody was determined to put an end to the depression.

"Pour yourselves a little drink," he said. "It'll warm you up good." I poured, and Carol and I drank. Woody stuck to coffee. Carol crawled into the back seat and covered herself up with blankets. She stayed awake only long enough to ask for a second cup of "coffee." She normally didn't drink much, and I knew that it would put her to sleep. It was the last we heard from her.

Woody kept reminding me to watch my side of the trail to see if our electrician was in either the ditch or the snow bank. We kept driving. Half an hour went by, and there was no sign of him. Pretty soon Woody asked,

"You've just about had it eh, Bev? Can't say I blame you. I hate to say it, but I'm glad your truck wouldn't start today. Just give me a few more hours, and then you can all go."

I looked at him to see if I'd heard right. "Yep," he said. "I gave them an ultimatum. Told them at the office to get another motor out here right now. An . . . we're having too many problems out at the rig. Probably need a whole new drillin' rig . . . its in such terrible shape . . . we'll see what this electrician knows about light plants. By that time Price will have the propane lines thawed out. If the new plant isn't here then, I'll lead the pack out. Told them that tonight."

Before I could question Woody on this, we spotted the electrician, or someone, standing in the middle of the road waving us down. When we pulled up and saw that it was a kid of about eighteen, I could almost hear Woody's mind saying "What does a kid that age know about a power plant?"

Woody rolled down his window and asked who he was. The kid's face was red and there was frost on his beard. I knew he was in for a bad time. Woody hated beards and disliked anyone from east of the Alberta border. This kid had an Ontario slang. It was easy to detect as he told us about his perilous journey to his very first rig job. Great! Woody told him to shut up and climb into the back seat.

"And don't sit on that girl who's sleeping back there," he said. We turned around and headed back toward camp. Woody and I drank the remains of the thermos and flask on the way.

The camp was dark as we drove in. Woody left us in the truck and went over to where Price and his crew were still working on the frozen propane lines. I'd heard a groan or two from Carol when the electrician got into and out of the truck, but she must have gone back to sleep. I pulled my blanket around me and before I realized what had happened, Woody was tapping on the window of the truck. "It's five-thirty," he said. "time you girls should be gettin' something on for brekky." I couldn't see anyone at the propane tank, so I assumed we had heat. Carol and I went into camp to begin still another day.

That day was worse than any which I had spent in this camp or any other. Tempers were so short that people were afraid to speak to each other. I gathered from rig gossip that there wasn't a second tank of propane on the lease, and the one we were using was about to expire. The electrician couldn't do a thing with the plant, and Woody said he was sure it was the first diesel plant the kid had ever laid eyes on. "He doesn't know his ass from a hole in the ground," was the way he put it.

Right after breakfast, Woody escorted the electrician down the road with a heavy tow rope and starter batteries to get him on his way. He was back within an hour.

I thawed out some stew and frozen buns for lunch. We didn't prepare anything else. The engineer, forklift operator and geologist arrived but sat at a separate table from the tool pusher. Everyone ate their lunch in silence. It was obvious there was dissension among the top brass, because Woody and any engineer who was assigned to the job usually got on well. The power problem was getting to us all.

Because of the propane shortage, I was careful with its use all day. I didn't bake a thing; I just sat by the stove keeping warm. Carol and I had a crying jag during the morning, but we weren't able to complete it because the power came on again. It seemed pointless to go on about having no power with lights shining down on us.

After the meagre supper I served up, Woody knew I was at the end of my wits. He came into the kitchen and said, "Go pack your gear. I'm sending you girls and some of the crew into Grande Cache 'til we get another propane tank out here and another power plant in operation. Price and Brent are staying to help me out." It was the best news I'd heard in a week. I didn't have to hurry to pack my gear; it had been packed for three days.

The rig hands had bedded down on the kitchen floor earlier, but when they heard the news, the kitchen cleared in one second flat. It was a mad stampede down the hall to their rooms. No one loved getting into town more than an off-duty rig hand. It was a long time before the trucks were started and ready to roll. When vehicles sit outside in very cold weather, it takes some time to jump-start them. It also takes a long time before they're really warm enough to be comfortable in, but we didn't wait for that to happen. We were on our way to town.

We left camp in a convoy of four trucks. Carol and I rode with the driller from the night shift — a quiet man who hadn't said much during our recent power outage. He was relatively new in camp, and it would be quite a while before he would venture even a good morning to us. We stopped three times to restart trucks stalled en route and arrived in the little mining town of Grande Cache at about 9:30 that evening. We nearly trampled each other getting into the lounge where we ordered doubles all around. It was the only way we could be sure of avoiding pneumonia or some other dreaded illness.

We stirred up some excitement as we entered the quiet lounge half filled with miners. There wasn't a woman in sight. It was also the only hotel in town where we were welcome. When we'd moved onto our present lease, three of our rig hands had been asked to leave the other hotels after brawls. Two of them had been put into the cooler overnight. They had been bailed out by our first tool pusher who received a stern warning from the hotel managers when he went to pay for the damages caused in the brawls. "Don't bring those rig hands back in here, ever again," said one. The second manager was more direct with, "I'll see you in court."

Our rig hands were not the only people who had been asked to leave bars and lounges in that little town. I'd heard stories about workers from other rigs in that area who had been in fights with miners. There were many reasons for these fights. Rig hands tipped better than miners, they were better paid than miners, and they were younger men who would fight at the drop of a hat. The bad blood was still flowing. I suspect there was another reason, and it was far deeper than these petty grievances. It was union-related. Rig hands were not unionized and had refused to become unionized, whereas miners were union members.

When our first round of drinks arrived, we placed a second order for doubles. The pretty waitress tucked away her twenty dollar tip; good service was ensured. We all sat around the table discussing the stupidity of office personnel, electricians, motormen in general, and light plants. We ran down every official in the entire oil industry. The choice of words was exquisite. We also discussed our miraculous escape from certain death by freezing and the superiority of rig hands over miners. The conversation was getting louder as each round of drinks was downed. Why I didn't go to my nice, warm room, I'll never know.

Carol and I ventured as far as the ladies washroom, but when I looked at myself in the mirror, the shock was terrible. Putting lipstick on in candle light is not easy, and my hair was a mess.

I'd rather forget the rest of that evening, but I'll relate the highlights — to the best of my ability.

The heat of the room and the doubles took their toll on all of us. I thought the room was turning awfully fast, and a couple of times I nearly fell off my chair. I could have gone to my room, but for some reason I stayed on with the crew. Looking back on that evening, I guess it was instinct: I knew there would be trouble. The chatter was continuous. My head began to nod until someone spilled a drink all over me and woke me up. One of our rig hands was crawling around under the table trying to find his room key. Another was trying to date the waitress who was the wife of the bar manager. He was glaring at all of us.

Just when I was searching for my room key among the silver, twenty dollar bills and glasses, the table suddenly tipped over, and everything crashed to the floor. Someone fell on Carol, and I heard a loud yell as she told that person to get his foot off her arm. When I turned around, I saw one of the miners at the next table jump up and begin brushing spilled liquor from his jacket. I backed up to watch the most beautiful fight I'd ever witnessed. It spread like wild fire across the room. Miners and rig hands were cursing each other in about ten languages. Because most of the rig hands were pretty drunk, they were slugging at anything that moved. Our nice quiet driller who hadn't said much in the ten days since he'd hit camp was right in the centre of the melee. He was using language that I didn't know existed.

Carol and I tried to get the attention of the crew, but it was no use. We backed up to a wall and watched. Soon the mirror behind us was hit by a bottle and crashed to the floor. It was time to leave. Just as we walked out into the lobby we met Woody. We watched as he stood in the doorway assessing the situation. It didn't take him long. He loped across the bar and grabbed a couple of rig hands by the shirt collar and shoved them into chairs. When they realized it was Woody, they shook their heads in disbelief, but they blinked themselves back to reality in a hurry.

I watched in amazement. Woody turned chairs right side up and had every one of his men under control in a few moments. He nodded apologies to everyone in sight and walked up to the manager who was behind the bar — probably the safest place to be.

I saw him take out his wallet and then return to our table, which had also been righted. There was broken glass and change all over the floor. Woody sat down and began a tirade about the behavior of rig hands in general. Before he was finished, the waitress had arrived with drinks for our crew. Other waitresses were serving drinks to everyone in the lounge. It was obvious Woody had bought a round for the house in an effort to restore law and order. I learned much later that he had also agreed to pay all damages and would formally apologize to anyone regarding the incident. I did see a few miners lift their glass in Woody's direction.

"Drink up everyone," said Woody. "We're heading back to camp. Seems like you guys don't know how to behave in town any more. No offense to you girls." He sipped his own drink and waited for his announcement to take effect. It did.

"Hey, Woody. I thought we were gonna stay in town tonight." And, "No way am I gonna go back to that iceberg of a camp." The young roughneck said, "We'll freeze if we go back to camp. I propose to stay in town." He lifted his drink to make his proposal and then tried to set it back down. He missed the table, and it landed on the floor.

The push never batted an eyelash. He grabbed the roughneck's arm as he reached for another drink and said, "I think you've had enough."

Woody broke the silence that engulfed the crew. "I just met a truck with a brand new motor on it. Guess where that truck was heading? Right into our camp. The propane guy arrived right after you people left and we'll have a nice warm kitchen again. We'll have steady power as soon as we get that new plant hooked up. Now I don't see any reason for staying in town, do you?" No one said a word.

To keep the conversation going, Woody added, "'Course that's the only way to get anything done around camp. Send the kids to town and out of the way."

He was getting a bit nasty. The rig hands began picking up their change and looking for their jackets which were scattered around the room. And I hadn't even gone to my room yet!

We drove back to camp and everything was in order, just as the push said it was. I don't know to this day how he managed to settle the quarrel in that lounge or how he managed to convince those rig hands to return to camp when they were all drunk. It took a pretty decent push to pull off a stunt like that, but old Woody was the best.

No one ever asked us why we hadn't gone to our rooms, and no one ever talked much about that evening in town. It was better to let it lie. We continued to sit in front of the old stove. The oven door never shut properly after that. The weight of all those feet and boots must have sprung the hinges. It was one of the oldest camps owned by that company, and every cook that worked in it was told they would get a new camp for the next well. I didn't stay around long enough to find out if they ever really did get one.

Chapter Nine

Gin Rummy

IF YOU DON'T PLAY GIN RUMMY, you just might not make it on the rigs. Gin rummy is almost mandatory in camp. A rig cook must be able to play the game well but not better than the tool push. She shouldn't really beat the camp attendant either or she won't have nice, clean sparkling floors or fresh laundry every day. If a cook does get out of line and beats the push a little too often, he somehow has to get back out to the rig because he's expecting a blow-out or a cavity to occur, or the rig hands are tripping and must have some supervision.

The push will not return to complete the game until he's sure his luck has changed. If he miscalculates and his luck hasn't changed, he then finds it necessary to go back out to his rig, because he's sure the crew on duty don't know their left hand from their right. He tells the cook that he'll return as soon as things are running smoothly again.

It's fine to beat service hands, rig hands, oil company representatives or other visitors, but don't beat the push or campy.

I worked with one campy who I couldn't beat anyway, no matter how often I tried. One might ask why

I was foolish enough to continue to play with an opponent who was so superior, but it was a matter of pride and necessity. Call it camp protocol or whatever. One shouldn't refuse to play a friendly game of gin with anyone who wants to, and one needs to play at least one game a day. I think it's called therapeutic or something like that, but I know it's necessary on occasion. It helps cement a relationship between a cook and a campy, and it keeps one's mind off other pressing concerns. Isolation in a camp out in the wilderness does strange things to some people.

Jerry, one of our campies, was a neat, tidy little man who kept things spotless around camp. He had a bad knee which allowed him to do the daily chores but which caused him great pain when his workload increased — as it does when it's time to move camp. At rig moving time, he had to be handled with kid gloves or Jerry would start to drink.

When Jerry took up drinking, he was impossible. A camp attendant is very important in camp; it's necessary to keep him happy. Playing a game of gin made Jerry very happy.

Jerry and I would often begin our daily game of gin right after breakfast. Because the entire game takes quite a long time to play, we would set it aside to be completed when it was more convenient for both of us. I did notice that Jerry nearly always found his work more pressing if I was a bit ahead of him.

He would always keep the score pad in his shirt pocket until we took up playing again. He would appear in the dining room at lunch time, take out the score pad, and lay it on the table beside the cards to see if I took the bait. If I had time, we would start again. The game would go on just long enough to see who would eventually win. If we completed the game, Jerry would circle the score at the bottom of the page and bring that score forward to the next page. It would be circled again in preparation for the next game. It was rig policy to pay up when leaving on long change or when you got fired or quit.

By the end of our two-week tour of duty, I would owe Jerry anywhere from seven to ten dollars. This figure would be neatly marked and circled at the top of the current page so that I wouldn't forget. Jerry lived in Edmonton and nearly always rode in and out of camp with me. We would always complete our last game the morning we were to go out on long change. He would check with me to see what time I would be leaving so he could work his schedule to coincide with mine. Sometime after lunch, and after packing our own lunches and a thermos of coffee and making sure that my shovel, chains and tow rope were still in the back of my truck, we would be ready to leave.

After being in camp for two weeks or more it's a real good feeling to be free and to be able to listen to a radio without static. We would ride along discussing the political situation, the state of the roads, and the latest rig hands and their related stupidity, but we would never discuss the amount I owed Jerry for the games of gin rummy we had played over the previous two weeks.

As we approached the highway where I would let Jerry off to catch his bus or to hitch a ride into the city, he would bring out the gin pad and lay it on the seat so that I could see it if I glanced that way. At that time, I would be very busy watching for traffic, and I always ignored the gin pad, much to Jerry's dismay. I think he spent those last few minutes of every trip out wondering if I would ever pay up.

When I came to a full stop, Jerry would gather up his gear and begin searching his pockets for his wallet. Then he would start mumbling something that went like, "I . . .uh . . . should pay you for half the gas . . . uh . . . but . . . uh." I didn't have the heart to put him through any more. I would then pick up the gin pad and exclaim over it, then reach for my purse to offer payment in full. Then Jerry would return his wallet, grin and say, "Well, Bev. You owe me eight dollars and ten cents and that's about half of what it would cost for gas. Let's call it square, okay?" This ritual took place every single time he rode out with me. He was a man of his word, and he believed that those who played gin rummy and lost should pay up.

Gin rummy was taken so seriously on rig camps that service and oil companies vied for being top dog in supplying the gin pads and personalized playing cards. If a gin game was in progress when a service company representative arrived, he would always check the game out to see whose cards or gin pads were being used. If we were using the opposition's cards and pads, he would then go out to his vehicle and bring in an armful of his company's latest playing cards, complete with company logo and matching gin pads. After all my years off the rigs, I've barely made a dent in my stack of playing cards and gin score pads, but then no one off the rigs plays gin like a rig hand.

Newcomers in camp would often bring other games out, but after a few tries these would be put away. Some cribbage was played and I even got into the odd game of bridge, but there is no game like gin rummy on rig camps. When anyone asks if you have time for some gin, they're not referring to the gin you drink. They are talking about the only gin any rig hand knows: gin rummy.

I've seen a gin game hold up a rig. I've seen service hands sit and wait while one of their crew completes a game which was started earlier, despite the fact that most service hands are expensive to have on a lease. It's strange that with all this seriousness, I never saw anyone quarrel or get angry over the result of a game of gin rummy. Rig hands will fight at the drop of a hat, but they won't fight over a game of gin.

Chapter Ten

A Rig Move —
A 'Moving' Experience

THE AVERAGE RIG MOVE goes something like this, if you're lucky. All hands are up before 5:00 a.m., everyone tells everyone else what to do, and tempers get shorter and shorter as the morning progresses. After everyone finishes breakfast, pantry shelves are securely packed, and all heavy objects are placed on the floor. The push drives back and forth from rig to camp in a desperate attempt to hurry both crews.

At the time I was on the rigs, moving was a very expensive operation, and the arrangements for a move were usually made over a mobile phone. A date for the move had to be agreed upon well in advance. If the push wasn't ready to move at that time, he would have to wait indefinitely unless he knew the boss of the trucking outfit.

The worst possible time for a move was in the spring. All rigs hoped to be moved onto a new lease before the spring thaw. If they hadn't moved by then, they would probably be racked until after spring breakup: the time when all roads in the northern areas of Alberta and some places in British Columbia become impassable due to muskeg and melting snow. At this time, travelling by road is banned.

Most of the roads I refer to in this book were just bulldozed trails which had been pushed through to get the trailers and rig onto the lease. This type of trail would be built in winter or during the very dry summer. Many rig moves had to be done with cats dragging truckloads of equipment and trailers off a lease or onto one. This was an extremely expensive, dirty, and horrible time for everyone on the job. In my books, there is absolutely no mud like Alberta mud. It's just plain terrible!

It should be noted that in the early Alberta oil patch there were very few paved roads north, west, or east of Edmonton. In fact, it was the oil companies that eventually built most of the roads — some of which are still not paved.

A recent trip around some of the areas where I worked in the 1970s proved to be very enlightening. Every road leading off the main highway, Highway 43 is paved as far as the eye can see. But my son and brother, who are both employed in the oil patch, tell me there are still quite a few muddy trails. And others are being pushed through every week. I'm referring to the still very isolated areas northeast of Red Earth and Zama. There is still a great deal of mud in that huge area of swamp and muskeg of northern Alberta.

The last chore I always did before the big move was to grab the coffee urn so that it wouldn't be under a table, along with fifteen other things, when we arrived at the new lease. I'd find out who had the water tank, with enough water to make coffee when we got there, so we wouldn't have to go looking for water. When I left the kitchen for the last time, it was a wonder I didn't break my neck when I stepped out the door. With all the noise from the crews breaking camp, one never knew whether the hallway platform would still be there. If the hallway platform had been taken down, it was a four or five foot jump down onto the ground, so we were always very, very careful when we opened a door to leave our kitchen before a camp move.

There would be a great laugh if I did fall flat on my face or fanny in the mud where the sidewalk used to be. Sometimes I'd yell or smile at a rig hand to help me down, and some roughneck would step forward and lift me down to dry ground. If he knew what was good for him, he'd carry me and the coffee urn over to my truck so that I wouldn't get all muddy.

I keep saying muddy, but it could have been snow. But then, in most rig moves, the snow turns to mud with all the turmoil of tearing out camp. When I think of rig moves, I still think of mud.

And then we'd sit, either in my truck or in the push's truck, waiting and waiting and waiting for further instructions on where we were going. The push would eventually saunter up to my window and tell us to get going down the trail before the trucks left and to watch for others coming in.

"Don't forget now," one push used to say. "I want you two in one piece when you get there, okay?" That was supposed to be funny — I think.

When I would broach the touchy subject of our destination, the push would say, "Just drive into Fox

Creek and wait for me there. We'll all go out to the new lease together. I'm not sure how that road is. "

I never had to ask where I'd find him in Fox Creek or in any other town, because after all those years in the oil patch I knew, beyond a shadow of a doubt, that all important business is discussed and settled in the nearest bar or lounge. During the seven years I worked out of Fox Creek, Rocky Mountain House, Grande Prairie, Grande Cache and other oil towns, every time I was to meet any tool push, or any other oil man, I met him at the hotel. I never even bothered to look in the coffee shops or restaurants; I always found the man I was looking for in the bar or lounge.

After collecting the mail and stocking up on personal supplies and reading material, my helper and I would go to the hotel lounge or bar, order a soft drink or coffee, and we would wait and wait and wait. Sometime during late morning or early afternoon, the push and a few of the crew would show up and we'd speculate on where we would be going. He would tell us he wasn't sure how to get there and would have to telephone the office for directions.

Meanwhile we'd leave the rig hands in the bar and go off with the push to wind up local business, such as presenting the bulk fuel dealer with either a case of his favourite whisky, a bottle of it, or a good dressing down — all according to how good the service was on the previous well.

The push would consult with us about the quality of the groceries and the way they were delivered before he would go into that store to talk to the manager. The push would end that business arrangement in much the same way as with the fuel dealer: if we were all satisfied with the business arrangement during the previous six to ten months, then he would hand out a bonus to the store manager; if we were not happy with the food, or with delivery of it, then there would be a dressing down and an exchange of some pretty harsh words.

Our push didn't believe in tipping anyone who didn't deserve it. But he was very generous to people who provided good service. He always kept in mind the possibility that we might be drilling a well in this exact area within a few months. It was like ensuring good service in the future. I always noticed the bulging brown paper bags when he left the store. There would be two boxes of fine chocolates, two cases of cigarettes, some expensive fruit, and newspapers and magazines. He always knew what cooks would really enjoy. Ah, but that old tooly was clever! Always keeping his fences mended was the way he looked at it.

When he completed his business, it would be back to the hotel to make that all important call. Then we'd all know where we were going.

So many times I remember sitting around a table in a lounge, or bar, quizzing the push as to how far off the pavement we would be when we got to our new location.

It was always, "Oh, not very far. It's gonna be a dream. Just wait 'til you see it. Just follow me when we leave the main road, and I'll take a look at the road before we drive in, okay?"

It appears that people who work in drilling company offices do not attend the same schools as those of us who work out there in the bush. When they told us we would be about ten miles off the pavement, it would surely be fifty. We would all head down the road in a convoy until we had travelled the required number of miles. Then the lead vehicle would turn off, and we would all follow. We would drive for miles along a pretty good road. Then it would turn into a pretty awful road, then a trail, and then a muddy mess that took a pretty skilled driver just to keep a vehicle in the ruts or between the ditches.

When the first truck got stuck, a conference would take place, and someone would have to walk down the road to where there was supposed to be a standby cat waiting to pull us through the mud.

If we were lucky and were able to get our vehicles right into the new lease, then the push would be yelling at us: "Get that truck out of the way. Park it over there in the bush somewhere, so it isn't in the way." On every new lease I've been on, there is barely enough room to turn a Volkswagen around, let alone a half-ton pickup truck. So I'd drive my truck right into the bush, and only God knew when, or if, I'd ever get it out of there again. All of us people who were low in the pecking order of rig life had to run our vehicles into the bush, leave them somewhere on the road coming in, or let a muddy roughneck move them for us. Somehow there was always room for the "important" people to park their trucks close to camp but hardly ever enough room for the cooks.

The next thing I'd worry about was water. Where is the well? Has it been dug yet? That was a foolish thought. Very seldom did I ever arrive at a new lease to find the water well in operation. It usually wasn't dug until after we had arrived and had begun ranting and raving over not having any water.

If everything is running smoothly, the truck carrying the light plant is among the first to arrive at a new location, along with the camp trailers. The average camp consists of six trailers which are set three in a row, about eight feet apart. This eight feet separating the trailers becomes a hallway with a floor and a roof made from sheets of plywood. These set into slots, or lips, on the sides of the industrial trailers. There are doors at each end when the trailers are all set in place. Jacks are used to put the trailers in exactly the right place. The rig hands must know what they're doing to get the sheets of plywood in place. Setting up camp is a complicated procedure done with a great amount of skill, swearing and yelling.

The shack which houses the light plant is placed just outside the cook's quarters so that she will be able to bitch about the constant noise over the next ten or twelve months while the well is being drilled.

It takes several days to set up a camp properly. During the first few hours, my helper and I would be in the kitchen asking every rig hand in sight if he knew where that turkey got to, the one who was hauling the propane tanks. We had to have propane to make coffee, and coffee is something everyone seemed to expect as soon as they walked, or climbed, into the kitchen.

If the propane had arrived and the rig hand with the water tank hadn't, then we'd go scouting for creek water. If it was winter, then I'd grab an axe to chop a hole in the ice first. Of course, the creek would have to be real close to camp, because every rig I was on was in bear country and I wasn't about to venture too far into the bush looking for water. If there wasn't a creek close by, then we'd just scoop up snow and melt it for coffee water. We seldom had time to pick all the pine needles or those little brown balls out of the snow. And then we'd have coffee — gallons of coffee: the drink that keeps the oil patch rolling.

The kitchen was impossible to move around in while it was being set up. There would be a dozen rig hands all trying to put the stove back together again so that we could light it. Once the stove was going, we picked up all the stuff that was knocked around en route and began the task of unpacking supplies. I'd be yelling for the campy and, if he had any sense at all, he would be stark-raving mad by that time — or drunk out of his mind. The campy must see that everything is in place after a move. Then he has to light all the furnaces, make beds for an army of truckers, as well as for his regular crew, and help get the kitchen organized. Moving day is when you know you've either got a gem for a campy or a fool. I've had both over the years.

By this time my helper and I were probably not speaking to one another. I'd have asked her to do so many things at once that she didn't know where to start. Most of my helpers were pretty cool. They would just carry on with whatever seemed the most important job at any given time, ignoring my temper outbursts entirely. After a rig move, they could usually be found unpacking the pantry and doing a dozen other jobs all at the same time. I'd be ranting and raving while digging around trying to find the frozen stew I nearly always served on rig moves.

I'd call a truce with my helper and the campy, and we'd take a cigarette break to discuss the situation which at the time looked absolutely hopeless. Thinking back on it, I wonder how in the name of God we ever got a meal together under those circumstances, but we did — every time. And, at the end, we were always still friends.

About this time, half the crew would be sent out to the rig lease to help unload the trucks bringing in the rig loads. The remaining crew would continue setting up camp. The hand who was left in charge, usually a driller, would sit inside drinking coffee and telling my helper and I how hard he was working. We'd be too busy to listen to him.

There would be many mouths to feed during a rig move: about thirty truckers and their helpers, the swampers, two crews of five or six men, the push, and often a drilling company superintendent or other brass from head office. There were always a few extras too, such as the truck push, a fuel hauler, three water well drillers and anyone else who had business on the lease. It wasn't uncommon to have sixty men to feed for at least the first week after a move.

My helper and I would need to look for a bush to hide behind until our water well was dug. On one rig move I ran into the bush and, in my haste, forgot to tuck my body shirt back into my jeans. I ran back into the kitchen and continued unpacking. I was beginning to think we had a bunch of fresh truckers, because every time I walked through the dining room, I could hear a snicker. When I turned to snarl at the trucker, he would look the other way. After a whole afternoon of this, I asked my helper what in hell was so darned funny, but she said she didn't know. When I was finally able to get into our quarters I saw what was causing all the humour, but I didn't think that it was such a funny matter. I stormed out of my room, scrambled up into the kitchen and asked my helper why she didn't tell me my shirttail was wagging. She burst into laughter. She hadn't noticed. A rig move was just too busy a time to notice such a mundane thing as the cook's shirttail.

Around 10:30 that night we would be able to call it quits and head for our quarters. If the water well drillers had been successful and we did have water, then taking a shower was uppermost in our minds. If the water well wasn't in production, then the drillers got a dressing down. Many of these men have been the brunt of some of my best cursing.

If, by any chance, the water well was dug and there was nice, hot water and we had been able to shower, we'd then hit our bunks and lay there wondering why we were there and how we were going to get through the next few days until we got spudded in. And then the crew, who were still setting up camp walkways and roofs, would be hammering and yelling at one another. They kept that up until I either got up and yelled at them to shut up, or they completed the job and left to help unload at the rig site. Ah, how sweet the silence was. Just the hum of the power plant — right outside my window.

Many truckers would be in camp for several days to help set various parts of the rig in place. A device called a cherry picker, which is operated from the deck of a truck, is used to complete this operation. The driver and his swamper would drag out the time as long as possible because one or the other of them was trying to date either the helper or myself.

Also, during this time, we would undoubtedly have a standby cat skinner and/or forklift operator around to pull loads onto the new lease or to unload mud or equipment. If the Cat camp was located nearby, this person would stay there, but usually he would be assigned a room in our camp. I had heard rumours that the meals were usually better at a rig camp than at a Cat camp. If this was the case, the cat skinner would pray for rain so that he would be able to stay at the rig camp until the rig moved out.

When the truckers finally left, another army of men hit camp. There would be fuel haulers, drilling mud haulers, geologists, mudmen or technicians, company brass, and a whole bunch more. To this day, I don't know who the others were or what they did, but they always showed up soon after we moved onto a new location. They were all required to sign the meal sheet, but it was obvious most of them were illiterate, because my helper, my campy or myself could never determine what companies they worked for or what they did. Our tooly always came to our rescue on that; we needed those names so that the companies could be billed and we could receive our rig-moving bonus.

Rigging up takes about a week or more depending on how good the push is, how competent the rig hands are, or how much mud there is to contend with. If the mud is too terrible, a machine called a Nodwell must be called in to rig up. During this time, I was too busy in camp to know exactly what they were doing out at the rig lease, but we would get all this important information from the roughnecks who came into camp.

The length of time it takes to drill an oil well depends on a lot of factors: the size of the rig — some are built especially for deep holes — the terrain, the abilities of the tool push and of his crew, and the number of unexpected breakdowns.

When the drilling company finally gets spudded in, drilling is continuous until the well is finished. The only break in drilling occurs when the testers arrive to determine how much further there is to drill, if there is oil and/or gas, or if it's a dry hole. Sometimes the testers are in and out of camp for weeks.

When the hole is completed, whether it's a producer or a dry hole, another service company takes over to either seal the well or put it into production. We did not often find out what the well had produced or if indeed it was a producer. Most of us experienced cooks knew that the well was a good producer if the "tight hole" sign was put up as soon as the testers arrived. If the tight hole sign wasn't up, then the well was probably not unusual. But then, we really never knew for sure. No one ever told the cooks what was happening . . . we had to figure it out for ourselves — if we were interested. I was usually so anxious to get out of camp by the end of drilling, I didn't really care what came out of the hole.

Then the whole operation starts all over again: another adventure, another rig move, another location, new people to meet, old friendships renewed and, on some occasions, a new romance.

Chapter Eleven

Shoot-out

DURING THE SUMMER OF 1974, I was working on a rig camp south of Whitecourt, Alberta: my home at that time. Whitecourt was considered to be an oil town.

Some of my readers might wonder if a Canadian oil town is like those in the States, where producing oil wells are located close to the outskirts of town. The only Canadian oil town that I know of which has producing wells close to the downtown core is Drayton Valley, Alberta. To me, what makes a town an oil town is a business core which is predominately made up of service companies, those that cater to the oil industry: well-testing companies, electrical companies, steam fitters, pipeline equipment, hotshot services, which promise fast delivery of all oil field needs, hardware stores, garages, bulk fuel stations, hotels and motels, cafes, lounges, and others. These services, along with other businesses, generate a booming economy.

I had been in this camp for seven months and knew most of the rig hands pretty well. The tool push, Murray, was in his late forties or early fifties but had only been on that job for a week. Murray, who was short, heavy, and partly bald, had a sparkling personality. He was the type

n who, upon entering a room, no one missed. He
. sort of charisma about him. And he had a gift for
handling his men — and his women. Everyone who knew
him liked him. He was well known in the oil patch and
had just returned from a long tour-of-duty in Iran.

Murray had replaced a tool push who just simply
had never came back from his long change. We never
really knew why he hadn't returned, but there were lots
of rumours. We were never able to establish facts to
support those rumours, but it was something to mull
over when we had nothing else to do.

Whatever had happened, most of us were very glad
he was gone. None of us had liked him anyway. The main
reason I didn't like that push was that we always seemed
to be short of roasts and steaks, large bags of sugar, flour
or cereals, or other expensive items from our grocery
order. Some of the rig hands said he was awfully stingy
with tools out at the rig which only supported our theory
that the push was stealing from his company. Company
theft was not unusual. In fact, I once heard a push brag
that, "It's a pretty stupid tool pusher that can't get away
with thirty grand a year in this job."

We were moving, and the new push didn't want a
new cook for this difficult job, so he asked me to stay
through the move. I fell for it. I let that crafty old tooly
flatter me into believing he "needed" me for the move.

So there I was, toiling away the last evening prepar-
ing sandwiches by the tub full, packing dishes, and doing
all the other things a cook must do to be ready for the
move. By daylight, a horde of truckers would descend
upon us for breakfast, and then we had to be ready to roll
by 8:00 a.m.

I was just about ready to call it quits when the new push strolled into camp and looked around. "Looks like you girls are pretty well prepared for the move. Oh, by the way Bev, the grub you've been putting out around here sure beats most camps I've been in."

I looked down from my little step ladder where I was securing shelves and grinned at Murray. "Flattery will get you everywhere."

"Why don't you knock off for tonight and come for a little ride with me. Have t'go into Whitecourt . . . only be there a few minutes. Got t'pay a couple of bills before we move out of the country."

I was very tired. I didn't know what to say to him, but I remembered I had a pair of glasses in town for repair and I really wanted to pick them up before we moved. "OK. I'll go. I've got a pair of glasses in town I'd like to pick up. The optometrist told me he would leave them at the desk in the Whitecourt Hotel. Said I could leave the cheque with the manager. Yes, I'd be glad to go along . . . just need a few minutes to comb my hair."

And that was the beginning of a great friendship and a whole lot of fun on every job where I worked on with that man. But first we had an adventure neither of us would ever forget.

I knew the push's trip to town had to be important. Pushes don't leave camp the night before a move when all the rig hands are tearing out. I suspected he had other reasons for going to town besides paying a few bills. The NHL playoffs were on, and most of us were hockey fans. Games and scores were discussed at every meal table. I really suspected Murray needed a good excuse to go to town late because he wanted to collect, or pay out, on an

NHL bet. Montreal and Toronto had just finished playing. Some of us had listened to the game on the radio.

I ran across to our quarters and told my helper where I was going. I even asked her to come along. I didn't really want to go to town alone with this new push but something told me it was all right. Besides he was a smashing fellow with an excellent reputation. I quickly showered and changed into clean jeans, a pullover, a warm jacket and boots and I was gone. The push was ready in his office with the door open. We hurried out into his truck without a single rig hand watching, or so we thought. And off we went to town: about 22 miles from camp on a pretty decent road.

We drove around to the bulk fuel dealers and Murray went in to settle the rig account. I saw them shake hands before Murray returned to the truck. He jumped into the truck with a grin saying he had one more call to make.

We drove across town to the local lumber mill, where the night shift was on duty. Murray ran into the manager's office without a knock. I saw a man push his wheelchair around the desk and go forward to meet our push. They shook hands, the manager smiled, and then he drew out his wallet. He took out a $50 bill and handed it to Murray. Murray took the bill and handed it back to the manager. Then they shook hands again. Murray bent down, hugged the younger man and ruffled his hair. I could see them both laughing as Murray walked out the door.

"What was that all about?" I asked out of curiosity.

"Oh . . . uh . . . it's a hockey bet. That's my brother. He used to play hockey . . . 'til he got hurt. Great guy .

.. he's still crazy about hockey. I won the bet so I donated the money to his hockey team. He..uh.. coaches a bunch of little guys."

I could see the push was very proud of his brother. He didn't say much more as we drove into town and parked at the hotel. The huge bar was almost filled with rig hands. We stood at the rear entrance door while Murray glanced around to see who he knew so we could sit with them. There didn't seem to be an empty table anywhere. Then a tall man with graying hair stood up and waved to us. It was the engineer off another rig that was drilling in our area. We picked our way around the tables, and the bartender came with another chair for us. After introductions were over I removed my jacket and put in an order for a tall glass of ginger ale and ice. Murray's eyebrows shot up in admiration of my choice of drink. Then I told him I was going to the lobby to pick up my glasses.

As I walked around the tables and chairs on my way to the lobby, I saw only two other women in that huge room. I marvelled at that and wondered again what I was doing in this job, in this place, and how long I would remain in this situation. I grinned to myself as I walked up to the desk. I had to admit I was having a lot of fun, but I had no idea what was still in store for me that evening.

I wrote the cheque out for my glasses and thanked the hotel manager for this extra service. Then I called my mom and my son on the pay phone before I went back into the bar.

As I pushed my way through to our table I saw, then heard, a ruckus at a corner table not far from ours. The language was terrible. I glanced at the man doing the shouting. He had long, greasy red hair and a sweatband around his forehead. We didn't have sweat bands in western Canada at that time, so I assumed the whole party at that table were not rig hands but visitors to our town.

I sat down at our table and all conversation stopped as we watched a shouting match turn ugly. Two of the "shit disturbers" were still carrying on the argument at the pool table. One pointed his cue at another who was sitting close. Then he knocked the man, a rig hand, out of his chair and the fight was on.

A country and western band was playing a Waylon Jennings song, and a few half-drunk rig hands, with very muddy boots, were on the dance floor dancing with two burly bar maids and a waitress from the cafe. She still had her apron on. They were all laughing and enjoying themselves. I looked at the sign, hanging by one nail on the stage that said, "No Muddy Boots On The Dance Floor." I don't suppose there was a single person in that room that didn't have mud on their boots. I smiled with wonder at anyone foolish enough to hang a sign like that in an oil town.

We all lost interest in the quarrel when the bartender arrived to settle the dispute. We could hear them talking about an NHL bet as well as a pool bet. The bartender told them there was absolutely no betting in that bar and if they didn't like the rules they could leave. Then they all sat down to another round of drinks — except one man, the tall redhead, who had slipped away and out the rear door that we had entered earlier that evening.

A few minutes later I felt someone bump my chair as he went by, and then the argument started up again. The red-headed man had returned. The bartender hurried over and, along with two other bartenders, escorted the redhead out of the bar. Everyone went back to their drinks and the babble of conversation got louder and louder. I yawned a couple of times and hoped Murray would be ready to leave real soon. I saw him watching me. I smiled at him and he leaned over to ask if I was ready to go. I nodded my head in agreement. He lifted his glass to indicate we would leave as soon as he finished his drink. And then the whole place went into an instant hush.

The red-headed man with the headband was standing in the rear doorway with a rifle pointed at the ceiling. He had a belt with a row of shells in slots all the way around. I stared in fascination; it was the only time I had ever seen a belt like that. I wanted to laugh; it looked so much like a western movie. I almost expected John Wayne to enter and settle the whole thing. I was frightened, but I was more astonished that this whole episode was really taking place. The man was walking slowly past the first table. He was about ten feet from me. I started to tremble all over, but I couldn't move or take my eyes off that man. And then the man looked right at me. I could feel my heart racing and felt my hands shaking as he went past us and stopped. He was only a few feet from Murray's chair.

It was a few minutes before I realized the band had stopped playing. It was incredibly quiet in that huge room. Then we heard the tall redhead say, "I came for my money . . . I won the bet . . . I don't give a fuck about your rules." He was talking to the bartender who had slowly walked up to face the man.

The bartender said, " Give me the gun . . . we'll settle our differences in my office . . . OK? Just give me the gun . . . please."

And then the gun went off. The vibration echoed through the room that had turned absolutely still. I froze in my chair. I couldn't move. I finally took my eyes off the man when Murray put his hand over mine and said, "Don't move Bev. Stay still."

I think he knew I was ready to make a dash into the lobby, but I was also afraid that any quick movement might trigger another shot. And then there was another shot!

We watched the bartender slowly back off, but he was still asking the redhead to hand over his gun. "I'll see you get your money. Just give me the gun . . . before someone gets hurt here."

With all the excitement I didn't see the policemen who were standing in the rear doorway. Their guns were still in their holsters. When the second shot thundered through the room, Murray and a lot of others tipped their tables over and got down behind them. I barely remember Murray putting his arms around me as we fell onto the floor to crouch behind the metal table. "Don't move for Christ sake," he whispered in my ear.

Another shot! I could see the policemen as they walked slowly into the room. One was standing right beside our overturned table. I saw him glance down at Murray and nod. Murray nodded back.

The gunman was backing out slowly. The policemen stood aside to make room for the redhead to leave the room. Then they would probably make a grab for him. I looked around but could only see feet and a few other people crouched behind overturned tables. I felt a sudden rush of tears, and my mind went wild. I had visions of my sons reading about their mother dying in a shoot-out in the Whitecourt Hotel bar.

I saw the surprised look on the gunman's face when he saw the policemen. He, like most of us, knew the cops wouldn't draw their guns in that crowded room. He kept on backing out. When he went past the policemen he pointed his rifle at them. They held both hands up to show the redhead they wouldn't draw their guns. And then it was all over. Murray stuck out his foot and tripped the redhead as he backed out past us. Both cops were on him before he hit the floor. The rifle fell onto the floor very close to us and slid a few feet before it came to rest by a pair of muddy boots sticking out from behind the table next to ours. Why it didn't go off I do not know. I felt the tears come. They stung my eyes and I cried — right there on that muddy floor. I was very glad to be alive, but I couldn't wait to get out of that place.

There was a lot of quiet conversation on our drive back to camp. I hoped there wouldn't be anyone around when we drove in. I didn't want to rehash that evening with anyone. I slipped into my room, crawled into bed, and thanked my maker for taking care of me in such a rough environment. I couldn't sleep. The whole series of events kept taking place over and over again in my mind. When I finally felt sleep taking over, it was after 4:00 a.m.

When I got up the next morning and started packing, Carol, my helper, asked me if I was glad to get my glasses back. I stood up with a start. Oh my God! I forgot about my glasses. I had absolutely no idea what happened to them when all the ruckus started in that bar. I had such a surprised look on my face, I knew I would have to give her an explanation. I had to tell her what happened, so I did.

"Well . . . for God's sake! He actually shot that rifle in the bar?" She was shaking her head with wonder. "If that isn't something . . . and you were actually down on the floor . . . behind a table?" She started to laugh.

"It wasn't funny. I was scared. So were a lot of other people." I said.

Yes, I had been scared . . . and a little ashamed too. What would my kids have thought if something had happened to me? In all of my adventures, I never wanted to bring shame upon my family's name. Then I started to cry. We both cried. And then we both laughed. Then we both got to work.

The whole gory episode was on the radio the next morning. The gunman and two of his friends were charged with selling drugs. They were also charged with being under the influence of those same drugs in a public place. Other charges related to the gun he was carrying and shooting. They were all from Ontario and were living in a small Ford van parked in a vacant lot near the hotel. I never heard the outcome of that incident because I never really wanted to know any more about it. I just wanted to forget the whole thing.

We had a lot of curious rig hands that morning who didn't really know if they should ask me about the incident that they were all talking about. In fact, some of them weren't really sure if they were supposed to know Murray and I had gone to town the previous evening — without a chaperon. It was a curious state of affairs. I had made my first wrong move in my rig career. I would be very careful from then on.

I think Carol straightened the rig hands out when I went to our quarters to pack my gear for the rig move. I was glad I didn't have to answer any of their questions, but there was one question I did have to answer — what was I going to do about my glasses? How was I ever going to get a new pair because they must have been smashed or broken in the clash of overturned tables. And if I did get them back, how was I going to tell my optometrist that I broke them again — this time in a shoot-out at the Whitecourt Hotel?

Chapter Twelve

Leaky Camp

I NO LONGER LIVE IN ALBERTA, but I still run into rig hands I've known over the years. I was coming out of a shopping centre in Lloydminster in the spring of 1985 when I was stopped by a young man who stuck out his hand and said, "Hi there. You're . . . Bev, aren't you?"

Not having been in the Lloydminster area for very long, but knowing it was the fastest growing oil town in the west, I suspected it was an old rig acquaintance. I took his hand and smiled at him. I couldn't remember his name so I asked him.

"I'm Willy. Remember me? I'm the guy that was sent in to clean up your quarters that time near Rocky. When the sewer backed up and you quit. When we had that Yankee push." He was grinning from ear to ear.

Oh yeah. How could I forget that little incident?

When I set out to write this book I seemed to remember all of the exciting times, the scary times and the fun times. This tour-of-duty was not one of those. It was a terrible time. It was so bad, I must have put the whole incident in my lost memory bank, but all it took was that friendly grin on that rig hand's face to bring it all into focus again.

We were on a deep well rig in the Rocky Mountain House area. The American drilling company was new in the area, and I believe this was their first well after coming across the border. Quite a few rigs were being brought into Canada from the United States at that time. The drilling was at its peak. It was late 1979.

The rig I had been working on for the previous year was racked, so my helper and I were looking forward to this tour of duty. The Rocky Mountain House area was beautiful, and with a deep well rig we'd be on the job for up to a year — we hoped. This would eliminate those dreadful rig and camp moves.

We were hired immediately. It was some time before we realized our folly. Neither of us had anything against Americans. We both thought they were just about as good as us Canadians, but what we didn't realize was that, in most areas south of the border, they don't use camps in the drilling industry. Most drilling is done in populated areas, and the rig hands drive to work every day just like any other working man. This was probably why they got stuck with that dreadful camp. They probably didn't know an old camp from a dead camp. This unfortunate fact was what nearly drove me away from the rigs a year before I finally gave it up for good.

I should have caught on a bit earlier, because the American push was allowed to take his long change and return to his home in Colorado while the rig and camp were set up by an old, experienced Canadian tool pusher who had been trying to retire for as long as I knew him. His name was well known in the oil patch, and he was always being called into service just to help set up camp or something else just as important — or so he said.

I enjoyed the first two weeks, but then the shit really hit the fan. Our old push went back to semi-retirement on his little farm, and the American returned.

It rained all through the month of June. The roof leaked in so many places we couldn't find enough containers to catch the drips. It was obvious that the company had been taken when they bought the old camp. It not only needed a new roof, it needed new just about everything. It was the worst excuse for a camp I'd ever been in.

Toward the end of the month, I took the push aside and explained to him he must do something about the roof or no rig hand would stay on that job. The push didn't take advice well and said he'd look after it as soon as he had time or when it quit raining. I left the name and address of a camp care outfit on the push's desk, hoping he would mobile and make arrangements for the work to be done.

July began with real hot weather and it continued to get hotter every day. At the end of the first week I reminded the push, at least three times a day, to contact the roofers so we could have the work done while the weather was good, but he always had other things on his mind. Personally, I think he didn't like taking advice from a woman.

Every day that old sun came out hotter than the previous day, and still there was no sign of the roofers. My temper was rising each day along with the sun. It was the hottest July on record, I think, and naturally the kitchen didn't have air conditioning. The push's quarters had air conditioning, as did the engineer's trailer, the mudman's trailer, the geologist's trailer, and even the extra trailer that had to be brought into camp to house the extra men on that hole. But the kitchen didn't have air conditioning and neither did our quarters.

Then to make matters worse, "some stupid son-of-a-bitch," as the push so often said, dropped a tool down the hole and we had to have a fishing crew in camp. If my memory serves me right, we had sixty-four men in camp for the last half of July and the first week of August. That was when they brought in the extra sleeper unit. We had to eat in shifts, and my meal sheet was three pages long. I couldn't keep track of the men that seemed to arrive in truckloads.

After the second week of fishing, a very expensive procedure, the hole caved in. A cave-in is so bad it would take a whole chapter to explain it ... although I'm still not exactly sure what it is. I do know it causes the push to become very excited. He curses and swears a lot, and there are a lot of very expensive people around as well as several water trucks and other experts.

If the crew is unable to plug the hole, someone from head office arrives. Then the activity, cussing and commotion becomes even greater. Our cave in was so bad we had experts from all over the country advising anyone who would listen how best to plug the cave in. With a fishing crew standing by and all those experts in camp it was a nightmare. It was so bad I couldn't corner the push long enough to remind him about the roofing job. That was a terrible error on my part.

When the roughy would come into camp for the rig box, I'd ask him how things were going. That was another mistake. When a roughy, who is so low in the pecking order in rig hierarchy, is asked his opinion on a matter of such grave importance, he will undoubtedly have an answer.

New rig hands know everything the first week in camp. One piece of valuable information he did offer was that he'd heard the push was afraid to come into camp because there were so many men around he was afraid I would take off. Usually when there were so many extra men in a camp, the cooks would have more help or extra pay. Needless to say, I was getting neither. The roughy also said the tool push was worried I would find out he hadn't had time to contact the roofers. Very interesting.

As it was still hot and there was no sign of rain, I'd kind of forgotten about the roofers myself because a more pressing issue had taken precedence. A terrible smell was taking over one whole trailer — the one that housed our quarters, the laundry room and washrooms. The campy and I had tracked down the source; it seemed to be coming from our quarters. My helper and I went right through the two rooms but couldn't find anything stale or rotten, so we took our problem to the only person in camp who would listen to us: the campy.

All three of us went through the wash house with a fine tooth comb, but we still couldn't find the cause of the smell. Then the answer dawned on Jerry, the campy — it was the sewer. We took our opinions outside and gingerly edged our way over to the bank. It was full to capacity from the June rains, and the pipe running out of the camp was at least a foot under water. During all that hot weather the muskeg had been draining into our sump. This was serious.

In Jerry's opinion, we had to have a new sump dug, because the environment people forbade us to drain any of the excess water away and it would soon be running over. We were in deep trouble. We sat there on the bank not saying a word. We all knew the push wouldn't know what to do, and with all the problems he was having at the rig he certainly wouldn't have time to listen to any of us at camp or understand how serious this problem was.

The smell got worse, and then the sump water started to back up into my room. Every day we'd put down more cardboard to soak up the moisture, but it was no good. Every day I tried to corner the push, but he was always too busy, he said, to talk about anything. Every day we'd try to get a rig hand, someone who counted, like the drillers, to tell Hans, the push, this couldn't go on. When we couldn't get anywhere with them, I even took my problems to the engineer, but I knew it wasn't his problem. We had to have a new sump dug, or we would be flooded out of camp. No one would listen to us.

When it finally got to the point that I couldn't stay in my room, I moved into the top bunk in my helper's room. The next day it started to seep into her room, and I stepped into this terrible smelling stuff that morning. I called it quits. As soon as breakfast was over, I told Shelly I was going out to the rig to talk to the push. She threw her dishrag in the sink and said, "I wouldn't miss this for the world. Wait for me."

In all the years I was on the rigs, I seldom drove out to the rig lease. I'm sure it was quite a shock for the push to see me and my helper drive right up to the engineer's trailer and catch them all inside playing gin rummy in their nice air-conditioned trailer — especially when they were always telling us how busy they were. We jumped out and I hammered away at the door until someone finally opened it.

The cards had been stuffed out of sight. The push asked what brought the two of us out there. I could tell at a glance that he wasn't impressed with our unexpected visit.

"It's about our camp, Hans. The sewer has backed up, and we can't stay in our quarters any longer the way it is. We have to dig another sump." I stood there waiting for a response. We both refused an invitation to take a seat but after being in that nice, cool trailer, I decided to state my opinion on that situation.

"Sure nice and cool in here. It must be great to have air conditioning, especially when you're so busy," I said. The four men in that trailer all took a sudden interest in the pattern of the linoleum on the floor. I'd hit a sore spot. They all knew about the sorry state the camp was in.

"Well now Bev, where do you think we're gonna get someone to dig us another hole right now? I'll look after that when we get this crisis over with at the rig." He pushed his chair back and appeared as though he was about to leave the trailer as was his habit every time I wanted something done. I moved over to stand in the doorway and then I really let him have it.

"While we're at it Hans, how about those roofers? Have you contacted them yet? If you don't do something about that sewer today, Hans, I'm leaving."

"And I'm going with her," said Shelly.

"And by the way Hans, it's gonna be pretty hard to get another cook to come and stay out here with a sewer problem and a leaky roof. For that matter, there won't be any reason for a cook to stay around. There won't be a man in camp in a few days." I stood in front of the door handle, but he pushed me aside and held the door open for me. When I realized he was offering me the door, I was furious.

"To top things off, Hans, it would be nice to have air conditioning in that hothouse too. I notice you've got it in your office and everyone else has got it but us." I left and made sure I slammed the door as hard as I could.

Just as I was about to pull away, Hans came out and walked up to the window of my truck. "I'll be down to camp in an hour or so and we'll talk this over then, okay? It should be obvious that I'm a very busy man."

I started to laugh at him. I couldn't believe what I was hearing. We drove back to camp. We were both about as depressed as anyone can get. It was at that point that I realized we were definitely at the very bottom of the rig camp pecking order.

We got lunch over with and still no push to talk things over. As was our custom, we rested for two hours right after lunch. With so many men in camp we were both tired and cranky and needed our rest, but we couldn't stand the smell in our rooms. I picked up my keys. Shelly grabbed her book and the mosquito dope, and we ran down to Jerry's room to see if he wanted to go with us to the creek where we often spent a pleasant afternoon when things were going better. Anything would be better than that smelly camp.

Jerry was acting very strange. He told us he was too busy to go, so we set off without him. Just as we approached the main road and about one-half mile from the creek, we could see a crew of our men putting a new culvert in where the old one had been crushed by the loads coming into our present location. A five-foot hole kept us from leaving our misery. I was so angry and frustrated that I was very near tears. We drove back toward camp. I got even more angry as I drove.

I went right past camp and on out to the rig again, past the engineer's trailer where we could see the brass all playing gin again, and on to the geologist's shack where we'd gone on one other occasion to play cards. I knew his trailer was air conditioned and he was a real nice guy who was well aware of what was happening in camp. He gathered up his rocks and samples, said we could stay as long as we wanted, and left us to rest in peace and air conditioning.

My helper climbed onto the top bunk while I crawled onto the lower one for a rest. It was sheer heaven on a day that was easily one hundred degrees in the shade. I lay there listening to the dreadful noise and marvelled at anyone who could possibly sleep that close to the rig. I tossed and turned and then gave up. I couldn't sleep. In a few minutes, I saw Shelly's face appear over the edge of her bunk.

"How in the hell do they sleep out here? I'll bet I can beat you at gin." She jumped down and we played gin rummy until the very last moment when we absolutely had to get back into the kitchen. Even without a sleep, we felt better having spent two hours in an air conditioned trailer.

Because of the heat, we'd prepared most of the meal earlier, but we still had the rig box to get ready and other chores to perform before the men came in for the evening meal. We took time to inspect our quarters, hoping for a miracle to wipe out the problems of our sewer. When I opened the door to our rooms the sewer water came rushing out around my feet. The last piece of cardboard was floating down the hallway. The smell was terrible. I slammed the door shut on the rushing water but it wouldn't catch. I yelled at Jerry but there was no answer.

I'd seen a bit man, a hotshot driver who delivers bits to rigs PDQ, drive past camp a few minutes before and then it hit me. Jerry had probably hitched a ride out of camp with him. I went to his room and found it empty. His gear was gone. I couldn't blame him. I was about to do the same.

When I returned to the kitchen, Shelly asked me what we were going to do next. I said, "We're leaving, right now." We both found rubber boots at the entrance and went into our flooded quarters to pack our gear. It didn't take long. We threw the bags into my truck, climbed in and were ready to leave that dreadful place, but first I wanted to give the push a last piece of advice.

I pulled up to the engineer's trailer and opened the door. They didn't have time to put the cards away this time. I casually looked around at all of them. They were very embarrassed, but I knew the embarrassment would turn into anger, very, very soon. Cooks on an oil rig do not walk in on top brass without knocking or without an invitation.

"We're leaving, Hans. I suggest you go down to camp and watch the sewer flood down the hallways. And the roof will be leaking as soon as those rain clouds reach this area. It isn't a nice place to be right now." I looked at all the brass and wondered who would be doing the dishes that night. " Oh, by the way," I added, "Jerry's gone already."

I couldn't believe what happened next. Hans waved at me to go back to camp and said, "Go on back to camp. I'll be there as soon as I finish this game." The bastard wouldn't believe we'd really leave him and all his men. I stood there in amazement. This couldn't be happening, could it? And then he said the crowning glory: "You're not going anywhere. The road's out. You can't get through." He grinned at me as though he was explaining something to a first grader. I turned and left before I started to cry.

I spluttered out to Shelly what he'd said and drove through the tears that wouldn't stop. As I approached the work crews at the main road I couldn't see the culvert so I assumed it was in the ditch. Then I got to thinking about the bit man and Jerry and knew they must have got through. I drove up as close as I could to view the hole. I could see they had most of the dirt pushed back into the hole, so I backed up and took a run at it. Shelly was hanging onto the door and we just sort of flew over that ditch with three of our guys standing there with their mouths open. I left them in a cloud of dust that would soon turn to mud. It had started to rain.

All the way to Rocky Mountain House, we discussed the stupidity of tool pushers — especially American tool pushers — engineers, fishermen, service hands and just about everyone who works on the rigs. Not once did we bring into our conversation how stupid we were for putting up with the situation for as long as we did, but it did cross our minds.

Like rig hands everywhere, we couldn't pass a bar without going into it. We pulled up to the favourite rig workers' hotel and went looking for someone to tell our troubles to. We found the bit man and Jerry deep in conversation. Jerry must have told that man everything, because when we arrived he was near tears himself, just listening to Jerry's sad tale of woe. We joined in and filled the bit man in on just how terrible it was out there — from a cook's point of view, of course.

We didn't have an answer when the bit man asked why some of our regular crew wouldn't take it upon themselves to fix the roof or contact the roofers on their own. It was a good question.

After a week of rest and leisure at my home in Whitecourt, we began wondering where we should look for another job. Shelly was about to leave for her home in the northern part of the province when the phone rang. It was our old tooly who had been called out of retirement again to complete the job on that ill-fated drilling rig and camp.

"You girls rested and ready to come back to work?"

"When did you come back? Are you at the rig now?"

"Yeah. Willy's got your quarters all nice and cleaned up. I ordered new rugs for the floor, be here today sometime . . . we've got a new roof on the camp and air conditioning on the way. Be here in the morning."

"Where's Hans?"

"Gone back to the States." I could almost see the grin on his face. I knew he was enjoying himself immensely. "When can I expect you?"

"Is Hans coming back?"

"No."

"We'll be there as soon as we can make it. How's lunch time tomorrow sound?"

And that's why we did go back and didn't leave the rigs for good that time. A camp is only as good as the push who's pushing the operation.

Chapter Thirteen

Another Well, Another Bear

THE PUSH WAS TELLING US about our upcoming rig move, and this job was just about at the end of my "rig" career. "Right on the pavement, nearly," he said, "and right close to your home town, Bev, at Whitecourt. Hardly any bears there."

The push was grinning at all of us. I didn't have the heart to tell him Whitecourt was still grizzly country.

There were bears everywhere we worked, it seemed. One of the few wells I worked on that didn't have a bear problem shocked us all on moving day.

The cat skinner was pushing a few trees out of the way, and he dug into a fairly young black bear's den. My campy and I watched the angry performance from my truck, where we were waiting for orders to leave for the new location. There sure wasn't anything sleepy about that bear when he tore out of his den and straight for the cat. All the rig hands quickly found shelter in the trucks until the bear decided to get on with finding another den. What shocked me the most was why that bear decided to den up so close to our camp?

If it wasn't grizzlies, it was black bears. They appeared as soon as we arrived and they stayed until either they were shot or we moved out. It doesn't take a bear long to become addicted to garbage. Even though we adhered to all the rules and regulations of garbage disposal, we still had bears. All my life I had been terrified of these creatures, and then I had to take up a job that took me right into their territory. Bears are something I've had a hard time dealing with since I was a small child.

We returned to the Goodwill district after that well near Whitecourt was completed. I was showing some evidence that I just might be able to handle another hole in bear country when our engineer asked my helper and I to go along one afternoon while he checked out a lease for the next well. It was late spring and we were both suffering from cabin fever, so we accepted his invitation. His truck was loaded with gear and a swamp buggy. The latter is an all-terrain vehicle which is used for trekking into muskeg. It has four very fat wheels and a flat deck which can carry quite a bit weight.

We declined the engineer's invitation to accompany him into the bush and opted for a spell in the warm sunshine near a half-decent road. He had parked on an old sawdust pile where a mill had operated many years before our arrival. It was a nice sunny day, so we spread out our canvas and pillows and I brought out our reading material and a thermos of coffee. We watched our engineer assemble his tools and gear for his foray into the bush. We waved good-bye as he promised to return in less than two hours.

Long after the two hours had gone by, he still wasn't back. We were always in the kitchen by 4:00 and it was already 4:15. We gathered up our canvas, magazines, and pillows and stowed them away in the back seat of the truck. I was more than a little angry with the engineer for not keeping his promise to return on time. We had to be back in camp by 4:30 at the latest to get the evening meal on. By 5:00 p.m. my anger had turned to worry. Worrying is something I'm very good at.

And then we heard him yelling. "Hey ... hey ... you guys. Get in the truck. Get in the truck." And then we saw him come out of the bush with a young black bear right on his tail.

When the bear saw the truck he stopped, but the engineer kept on coming. His vehicle hit the side of the truck and he went head-over-heels into the back of it. The vehicle fell back upside down onto the sawdust pile. The wheels were spinning in mid air. There was mud everywhere. The engineer's face was covered with it. He kept motioning for me to start the truck and get out of there. I was so flabbergasted, I sat there looking at the bear who was looking at us. He was snarling and moving his head back and forth like a polar bear. The engineer was pounding the top of the cab yelling at me to get going.

I started the truck but in that small area I had a hard time turning it around. We finally got turned the other way and that bear was still standing there shaking his head at us as we drove out of sight.

The whole incident took the starch out of me, and I couldn't drive any more. My knees were shaking and I was blubbering and stammering. I stopped the truck and the engineer climbed down from the back and got into the cab. He was pretty badly shaken up. I could see his hands shake on the steering wheel. He dug into his glove compartment for cigarettes and then the bear showed up again. He was right beside the truck snarling and growling. The slobber was hanging from his huge jowls.

We left without loading the machine that day. When we arrived back in camp an hour late, we were all so upset we could hardly get our story out. But out it came and for once, all three of us told the same story. I declined the invitation to accompany the engineer into the area to pick up his all-terrain vehicle. So did my helper.

Chapter Fourteen

Sling Shot

MORE WELLS HAVE BEEN DRILLED around camp kitchens than any other place — except, perhaps, a bar room table. Camp kitchens have also seen the muddiest roads travelled, the largest grizzly bears seen, and the fastest "trips" and the longest fishing expeditions accomplished. Some stories are hilarious, and some are out-and-out lies, but some do have a bit of truth to them. No one can tell a story like a rig hand.

At this point I'd like to remind my readers that in the "good old days," before most rig camps had satellite dishes, we had to provide our own fun. We watched old movies or taped programs; we hunted and fished, we read lots of old magazines and Zane Grey novels; we played board games and, of course, gin rummy; but apart from these activities, there was very little else to do in our spare time. So we sat around drinking coffee and telling stories. Soon the stories got out of hand and became out-and-out lies, but it was fun — I think.

This story is about me.

I was coming into a camp after my week out when I got stuck, as usual. I sat most of the day from about 11 a.m. until nearly dark. I had rocked my truck back and forth so many times I just slid further into the ditch. Finally I realized I had to give up and simply wait for someone to come along. Someone always comes along on a rig road, sooner or later.

That someone turned out to be a trucker with a load of drilling mud for our rig. It was quite dark when he pulled up behind my truck and walked up to my window.

"Hi there. Looks like you're stuck pretty good there, lady. Been here long?"

Standard questions. I watched him as he reached for his cigarettes, then take out his lighter. He offered one to me and watched me as I took it out of his package. I couldn't see his face, but I had the feeling I had seen him before. But then I had seen many truckers on many different rigs. Most of us had a nodding acquaintance with each other, but names were hard to remember in the patch.

The tall trucker lit our smokes, drew a flashlight from his pocket and said, "I'll take a look and see if I can pull you out." He walked around my pick-up and was soon back at my window.

"Don't see how I can pull you out in the dark. Might damage something underneath . . . hard to put a chain on in the dark and you're down pretty deep there . . . in the mud." He stepped a bit closer and smiled at me. "Wanna ride in to camp with me? Your push can send someone out in the daylight so your truck won't be damaged . . . nice little vehicle you got there . . . or is that your husband's truck?"

"No, it's mine . . . Sure, I'll ride in with you. I have a few things in the back, though. Do you mind . . . is it OK . . . to bring them along?"

"Sure, go ahead, I'll make some room in the cab. Got my stuff all over the seat."

He left and I got out of the truck, locked it up and hurried into the canopy for my gear. As I pulled my bags to the door of the canopy, I saw the trucker had returned and was lifting my gear into his cab. After the third trip he said, "Sure got a lot of gear here . . . what do you do with all this . . . uh . . . stuff? How long do you girls stay in at a time, anyway, a year?"

He was grinning as he watched me lock up the canopy. He took the heavy bag from me and helped me into the cab of his truck. As he walked around his truck, past the headlights, I noticed he had a limp. Then I heard him open his door to get behind the steering wheel. He said he'd dropped something; then I heard him laugh. "What the hell is this? Is this yours?" He was holding up my slingshot and laughing. The cab door was open, so I got a better look at him, and he got a better look at me.

I felt my face go red, but I laughed with him as he got in and started up the truck. We drove along while he shifted gears and we slid along about ten miles an hour in the mud. Then he looked at me in the dim glow of the dash lights. "Sort of a long way out here, isn't it? My name's Paul. Think I've seen you before . . . somewhere. Couldn't forget a good-looking woman like you . . . I don't think." He was back watching the road. I was suffering from embarrassment and hardly knew what to say to this charming man, so I didn't say anything at all.

"Just out of curiosity, what ya got in all those bags? How long did you say you girls stayed in camp, two weeks or three?".

"Two."

"Most people I know who work on the rigs take stuff out of camp, not into it, right?" He smiled at me again. "And just what in the hell are you doing with a sling shot?"

"Oh, I do lots of stuff. Some of the guys take us out shooting game birds. I do a bit of target practice with the water hauler when he's filling his tank. He's the guy who made it for me. And I practice a bit at home . . . in the basement. Actually, I'm pretty good with it." I smiled right back at the driver. He was lighting another cigarette. He handed over his lighter for me to use, as I was opening a carton from my gear. His hand touched mine, and I knew it was deliberate. It was not an uncomfortable feeling. I lit my smoke and handed him the lighter. Our hands touched again, only this time it took him longer to take his lighter. I reminded my self to be careful while playing this game with a strange man in a truck cab a long way out in the wilderness. And then we saw the lights of camp. I was quite relieved and started gathering my things.

"Lady, I sure hope I see you again. It was sure nice to give yuh a lift." He stopped the truck and helped me in with my gear. I could feel his warm smile even after I watched him drive to the rig lease to unload before his return down that long, lonely, muddy road and out of my life . . . I thought.

I completed that job over the next five months, then two more in the same area, and then I was asked to go to the new area around Rocky Mountain House.

It was summer and a beautiful day when I drove into that brand new camp. I went to relieve a cook who had broken her wrist in a fall. The cook's helper was an elderly woman who didn't want the responsibility of my job. She was due to retire as soon as I could find a helper and a campy. Her husband was the current camp attendant, and they had both decided to leave the rig camps. This was too good to be true: a brand new camp and my choice of helper and campy. Oh, how I hoped we had a good tooly.

I glanced at the food on the stove and on the back table and hurried to my quarters across from the dining room. I threw my gear in, grabbed an apron and went back into the kitchen to help serve lunch. I was astonished at the meagre meal put out for the men. The back table had three pies that looked about a week old. They were pumpkin and the filling had fallen away from the crust. I knew I didn't have far to go to improve on the meals in that camp.

At lunch time I smiled at the men as they inspected me from across the tables. I wondered which one of them was our tool push. Then a short stocky man who was partly bald walked into the room and announced that he was the new tool pusher. It was Harvey, a man I had worked with on many rigs during the first three years I was in the oil patch. He had just returned from Iran. We both smiled and I think we were both glad to see each other. By the look of the food, his men would be quite happy to have a good cook, and by that time, I was a pretty darn good cook. Harvey was a very good tool push to work for.

I quickly got a batch of buns going along with a roast beef supper complete with apple and raisin pie. I was sure the cinnamon buns would melt any rig hand's heart. I also knew Harvey would inform his men that I knew how to cook.

When the night shift lined up at the stove for their supper they were all curious to see the new cook and, what was more important, to see what she put out for supper. Without a word they ate their meal and left with another plate full of pie and cinnamon buns. My helper and I sat down to wait for the roughneck to come in for the rig box and for the brass to come in for their evening meal.

We didn't have long to wait. The meal box was ready to send out as soon as the roughneck arrived, and the brass came in the front door soon after. We sat down to eat at the front table while all the others, about nine of them, ate their meal in silence. They all watched every move I made, and I was quite sure every man in that camp knew what my name was, that I was single, what size bra I took, how much I drank, or if I drank at all, how I conducted my life in a rig camp and that I had worked for Harvey before. That should have said it all. People didn't work for Harvey for very long unless they were very good at their job. I got up from the table after completing my supper and was almost certain that all nine men watched me leave that room. I hurried into the kitchen and grinned at the helper who was doing dishes.

"You made quite an impact out there Bev. Bernice ... she's a pretty good cook ... I'm not. It's time for both of us to hang up our aprons. These guys are too hard to please, anyway." She was not bitter, only making a statement.

By the time our dishes were cleared away and we put out food on the back table for truckers or other people doing business in camp, I heard a lot of noise and chuckling in the dining room. My helper was just going out with the evening coffee urn, and I was right behind her. It would be a half-hour before the coffee would be ready. There was a lot of scuffling and laughing while ten men decided to find partners for two double games of gin rummy. Harvey walked in, demanded to get in on one game, and asked me to be his partner. I couldn't refuse. It isn't nice to refuse a game of gin on the first invitation . . . especially if it is from the boss at a new job.

The game was nearly over when the door opened and a tall good-looking man with a limp stood in the doorway. He looked familiar. He was looking right at me, so I smiled and nodded. Harvey looked up at me, then he looked at the man in the doorway. He turned back to the game but turned around again when the tall man asked who the push was.

"Right here. I'm the push. What can I do for ya?" He didn't get up to say hello, and he didn't put his cards down. That was Harvey's way.

"Could ya sign this for me? I just dropped off a trailer with drillin' mud at the rig. We don't need the trailer now. Can piggy back it out when the roads are better. If that's OK with you, of course."

Harvey asked the trucker to sit down while he signed the freight bill. Then he asked him if he wanted a bed.

"No thanks. Just gonna have a coffee, if it's OK with the cook there, n' some of that pie . . . if ya don't mind." He was helping himself to pie and coffee. I noticed his limp, and I kept wondering where I'd seen this man before. I just couldn't put a name to him. He was very

ـoking and I wondered why I couldn't remember
. handsome man's name. I grinned to myself and
. d the last hand of a losing game of gin.

When we put the cards away, the rig hands got into
some pretty heavy discussions on mud viscosity and
blow-out preventers, and then someone said they'd seen
a bear on their way from the rig.

The push got up to pour himself a coffee and asked
the trucker to sit down. He said he'd sooner stand. "I sit
all day, I need t'stand awhile," he smiled at the push, then
at me.

There were several smutty jokes told, and I got up
to go to my room. When I got to the door the trucker put
his arm across and stood directly in my way. He smiled
down at me and I couldn't help notice his long, dark
lashes. This guy was very good-looking.

"Hi there", he said very quietly. "Remember me?"

"No . . . I don't, honest. I know I've seen you
before." I made a feeble attempt to go around him, but
he moved just enough to make sure I couldn't. I stood
back from the door and prepared myself to go through
the kitchen. He knew exactly what I was going to do.

He said, "I've got a story to tell you guys." He
grinned at the push and then at me.

"And you . . . there . . . pretty lady."

He took my arm and sat me down, and then sat
down very close to me. I know now it was to be sure I
didn't leave the room.

He started up again, but there was too much noise.
The push yelled at them. "Shut up you guys, Paul here has
somethin' to say." He got the attention of everyone in the
room.

Paul began, with a sheepish grin. "A friend of mine up north told me he had a cook, a rig cook, that got herself and a whole crew of hands kicked out of a bar in Edson one night. He had the attention of every man in the room. I was wishing I was any place but in that room. I could feel my face get red and my heart came up into my throat.

"Yep, and do you guys know why they all got kicked out of that bar?" He was really enjoying himself.

No one said a word.

"It's because that cook shot a light out in that bar." The guffaws and hoots were so loud the trucker couldn't go on with his story. When the noise died away he said. "And do you know what she shot that light out with? A slingshot! Yep . . . a slingshot. Got every single man on that shift kicked right out with her! And . . . listen to this, you guys, the bar manager even confiscated . . . "

He couldn't go on, he was laughing so hard. ". . . the weapon . . . uh . . . the slingshot, it was confiscated. The bartender kept it for . . . well over six months. Then the push went into town and got it for her. Didn't have to pay a fine or anything. They probably didn't know what to do with that kind've weapon . . . but he did get it and brought it out to the rig for her."

The trucker was having a ball. I was becoming very embarrassed and was waiting for an escape from that room. But that was not to be.

"And that's not all boys and girls. Do you know what she did then? She took the whole crew to the curling rink . . . where they had some kind of a lounge or bar. It seems that cook knew her way around that town. That

127

crew sort of enjoyed that lounge and kept going there 'til they all got kicked out of there . . . on their own."

The trucker was looking at me all the time by then. I didn't move because up until then I don't think the guys in that room knew it was me that Paul was talking about . . . yet.

"Yes . . . that camp was a roughneck's dream and a tool push's nightmare. Only a half-mile from town. First time in over ten years that push had drilled closer than forty miles to a town . . . and then to have that happen . . . sure was lucky he had a cook that would do that for him . . . get his crew kicked out of a bar . . . so they'd get to work on time."

There was a lot of noise now so Paul went on.

"Say there . . . uh . . . pretty lady. Didn't I hear you say you were from the Edson area?" He was smiling through those half-closed eyes. "And wasn't that a sling shot you had in your gear that time I gave you a lift into camp . . . up north that time?"

And then there was a real hullabaloo. All the guys looked at me, then over to Paul, then to the push, and then they all laughed. And did they laugh. They all had one great big joke on their new cook. It was sort of hilarious all right . . . I had to admit. So I started to laugh too.

Then they were all asking me if I really did shoot the light out, and why, and could they see my slingshot, and so on. I explained that, yes I did shoot the light out and that I did have my weapon with me. I told them a bit about that incident, I almost had to by then.

I said that I had used it that night on the way into town. A lot of guys on our rig at that time had slingshots. We scared up a bunch of partridge on our way, and we all got out to shoot them. One roughneck borrowed my weapon, and when we got the birds skinned and put in bags, he forgot to return it to me. When we got to the bar, I forgot about it until one of the guys brought it out to show some rig hands from another rig. The new rig hands examined it and laughed about it and joked about it belonging to a cook. Then the driller asked if I could actually shoot a partridge with that . . . weapon.

"Of course she can!" My crew had jumped to my defense and had gone on to say that I could probably shoot a light out right over the bar. When they asked me to try, I said sure . . . if I had to . . . and . . . if they'd bet enough money on it. So, I took a marble out of my purse, lined up, and shot the light out.

One of the younger roughnecks who had been listening to my part of the story just stared at me, and then he laughed, "You really did shoot that light out then."

He shook his head, stared at me with admiration and then left the room. Harvey waited until they were all gone. Then he got up and asked if he could pour me a coffee.

I said sure and wondered if he was going to fire me or lecture me or what. But soon I could see he was having a hard time holding his laughter. And then he slapped me on the back and said, "Congratulations! I sure hope you won't shoot any windows out around here. Is it going to be safe for me to come into camp now with this . . . uh . . . weapon? "

He was having a wonderful time. We all stood up, and I excused myself. Paul stood in front of me again, and I couldn't leave. Then he put out his hand and I took it. He put the other hand over mine, and then he looked at me with those gorgeous eyes . . . through those long lashes. I just about melted.

"You sure are a good sport. I just couldn't *not* tell on you. Ever since I met you, I've wondered about you and that slingshot."

I smiled, took my hand back and left the room. I could still hear the push and the trucker chuckling as I entered my quarters to end a very exciting day on a brand new rig.

Chapter Fifteen

Farm

DURING MY "RIG" YEARS, I lived in several places: first in Edson and then in Whitecourt. My first home in Whitecourt was a brand new trailer, which I put on a lot in a downtown trailer court — a rundown dump with dusty roadways, poor garbage pickup, and no street lighting. The noise of the night included fights and gunshots. Every night, the police made a few trips around the 45 trailers, and often they were called in to settle a fight or a domestic dispute. It was not a good place to live, but it was the only place in town that I could get. During the oil boom years, rental units of every kind were nonexistent, and only a few houses were for rent or for sale. One had to take what was available.

My youngest son, who lived with me at the time, worked at the downtown theatre as a projectionist. He didn't drink or use drugs, so he kept to himself. Both of us hoped to leave the trailer court as soon as we found another place to live.

Later that year I bought a small acreage about nine miles northwest of town. I spent a lot of time on my week out driving back and forth from the trailer court to my property where I eventually planned to move our trailer.

I was seeing a very nice man who had the good sense to work a nine to five job for Hudson Bay Gas & Oil in Fox Creek. He helped me dig holes to plant a row of trees which I hoped would one day be a wind break, and he helped me plough up a bit of pasture for a garden.

My acreage, which was a 3.4 acre wedge, included a ravine which was covered in quite a few trees, a lot of underbrush, and even lilacs and caragana bushes which had gone wild. A small creek ran down the ravine, meeting a larger creek at the narrow point of the property. Because it originated from a spring, the creek ran all year long.

There was an old log barn near the main gate. The underbrush was thick around the barn and the gate. The entire acreage was fenced and leased to my closest neighbour as a pasture for his cows. In the fall, we just opened a small gate in the wire fence between our properties so his cattle could get through.

Everything went fine the first year. I even made a few dollars selling the hay off my land before the cows were let in for pasture and after my garden was harvested.

Some of my rig friends came out one Sunday to help my friend, my son, and I in the garden. It ended up being a real work party that day. I had bought a lean-to porch from a man whose trailer had burned a few doors from mine. It had been hauled over on a low-boy and set on a plywood frame my son and I had built for it. Our project that day was to side the porch so we would have shelter when we stayed overnight. It was also a place to store our tools.

The gang arrived before noon and started to dig a hole for an outhouse. One of my rig friends from had brought a toilet out on the back of his truck — just what we needed out there. The well drillers came out that same day to drill a water well, and my son and I had a barbecue that evening for all our guests.

The garden was doing well and the hay was about four feet high. Several times during that morning, when it was still very quiet, I thought I heard something running in the hay field. The second time I thought I heard a grunt. When I mentioned this to my son Murray, he said he had heard those noises too. "Probably the neighbour's dog . . . or a pig maybe . . . " He wasn't really interested; he was too busy getting a suntan.

I didn't hear the noise again during the rest of that day, but with so many people around I couldn't hear anything except laughter over the game of pick-up ball they were playing. We had a campfire that evening, and everyone left before midnight. Murray and I had planned to stay overnight if we got the porch sided up. We had brought air mattresses and sleeping bags, and it was a beautiful moonlit night. Murray chose to sleep outside, so I left the door open and I was soon asleep.

I heard Murray come in and shut the door. "What's wrong?" I asked.

"I heard that noise again. It sounded like a pig or something. It couldn't have been a bear, could it Mom?" He was a very big man and didn't like to appear timid, but I knew he was afraid. Murray hated bears almost as much as I did.

"I don't think so Mom. I sure hope not anyway."

I went back to bed, but I couldn't sleep. I had one thing on my mind — bears!

My next project was to build a better gate out onto the road. As we left the following evening, I measured the length for the rails that I would need, fastened the wire hook around the worn-out post, and headed for home. My son had to work the next day. I still had three days left on my long change.

I loaded up my lumber supplies early the next morning and headed out to the "farm," as I had begun to call my little acreage. As I pulled up to the gate and stopped to open it, I glanced at some grass that was flattened out near the brush. It was obvious that an animal of some kind had been travelling through the grass and onto the ravine trail. I crawled down that trail as far as I could until I got all tangled up in old barbed wire and caragana bushes. Then I backed out, got into my truck, and drove through the gate to unload the lumber. I pulled and pushed it all out of the truck canopy, and then I turned around and drove away from the gate. I left it open, as I was only going to talk to the neighbours about harvesting the hay again.

His wife was the only person around, but she told me they wanted the hay and then the use of the property for pasture . . . same as the year before. I drove back to my place. As I turned in, I saw a pretty good-sized bear come out of the hayfield and then go down the little trail I had investigated earlier. I slammed on the brakes, put my head on the steering wheel, and cried. Then I got mad. I drove my truck through the gate, stopped, got out, and proceeded to make a lot of noise. I was going to build that gate in spite of that damned bear.

As soon as I got the planks laid out where I wanted them, I looked for my hammer. It was in the truck. I grabbed it and ran back to my work watching for the bear all the way. I got one nail in and only hit one finger. I forgot about the bear for a minute as I hopped around yelling and holding my sore finger. Then I started pounding away at a second nail. Just as I raised the hammer for the second or third time, the bear came back. He was very bold. He kept coming closer, so I headed for the truck. I bumped my head and hurt my sore finger when I opened the truck door in such a hurry. The damned bear was right behind me. I was very surprised he would chase me like that. I sat for a long time nursing my sore finger and my headache and doing a lot of heavy thinking.

I drove the truck up close to the barn where I had piled some old lumber and brush. I had planned to burn this pile as soon as I had obtained a permit. I grabbed my lighter and a chunk of newspaper from the truck seat and lit a fire.

A fire would certainly scare the bear away, I kept telling myself. As soon as I lit the fire, I knew I shouldn't have done so. There was a huge fine for burning without a permit; Whitecourt is in forestry country.

I sat there trying to decide what to do. I certainly couldn't work on my gate with that bear hanging around ready to do me in, and I couldn't spend the whole day sitting by a fire worrying about the gate and the bear . . . or could I?

The decision was made for me. The brush was very dry and it caught fast. I very soon had a blaze going that could be seen for miles. I hung my head and wondered where I had stored that bottle of rye. I knew I would have the forestry people out as soon as someone reported the blaze or saw the smoke. Oh why did a bear have to take up farming with me anyway!

I soon found the rye. The forestry plane flew over. I knew all the pilots, and they knew my old barn. It was on all the forestry maps in the area. I watched my fire burn itself out while I drank rye and wondered how much my fine would be. I also wondered when the bear would return. I was glad when it started to rain. That would solve one of my problems. It was a depressing, dull, rainy afternoon.

When the fire was nearly burned out, I wondered where I was going to get water to pour over it. There were several old logs still smoldering, and I knew they would stay that way for a long time unless I could water them or cover them over with dirt. The rain had stopped, and I knew I had to make darned sure that blaze was out before I left my place. God help anyone who was careless in that country of trees and trees and more trees.

I went to my truck to get the shovel, and there was the bear again. He must have snuck up on me. I screamed and ran back into the truck. And, of course, I bumped my head again. It was the third time I had bumped my head that day. Between my headache and my sore finger, I was a sorry sight. I beeped the horn until the bear went down his little trail by the gate. Then I sat and cried until the last spark of fire died down. I drove my truck out of there and didn't even stop to shut the gate. I really didn't care what happened to my dream of country living. I drove back to my neighbours to ask them if they had seen a bear around. I was also going to ask them if they wanted to buy my place, but I changed my mind.

"See any bears around this summer Mr. Halliwell?" I asked.

"Saw one this spring. A young one . . . about a two year old. He was pretty big though. I think that was the bear that took one of Bruce's calves." He pointed west where his brother Bruce lived. Haven't seen him since."

"Well I have. He's in that little ravine. I've seen him three times at the gate. Do you know that bear charged me?"

"I'll be damned. Charged you eh?" Mr. Halliwell removed his hat and thought a bit. "Surely a young bear that age wouldn't charge you! Really?"

"It sure did."

I turned on my heel and left that old fool who wouldn't believe me. I was so angry that I spun my tires and left his gate open. I drove to town and straight to the real estate office where I'd purchased the property.

"So you want to sell your farm, Bev! Not what you wanted eh?"

We came to an agreement on price, and I signed the paper to allow them to show the place. I knew it would sell; there weren't many small holdings left around Whitecourt by that time.

I walked out of that office without telling the agent the property had a resident bear. I left that for the new owner to find out. I went back to the rigs for another four years and many more bear encounters before I finally saw the light and gave up the rigs and bears for good.

I finally moved to a small city in the Okanagan Valley, B.C., where there are hardly any bears.

Chapter Sixteen

Dennis

PART OF THE EXCITEMENT of going to a new rig was speculation. Will there be anyone I know on the job? Will we have a decent tool push? Will the guys be easy to please in the food department? Usually the guys took their cue from their driller or the tool push. If there was a good push in camp the job would probably be fun.

And then there was always the possibility of meeting the right man. My helpers and I were single and were almost positive we didn't want to become involved with or to marry a rig hand. It was too risky. Their hours were terrible, and their work was dangerous. Yet both of us had met some pretty exciting men so far.

It was almost impossible to conduct a relationship at a rig camp. My helpers and I wanted to keep our dignity and our reputations, but we speculated a lot. We were very much aware of the attention and open invitations of many interested rig hands. Temptation was always very close at hand. Then every once in a while we'd get a terrible jolt, and we were almost afraid for our lives.

Early one spring, I was sent to a camp northwest of Grande Cache to a rig that was lucky enough to be spudded in before spring breakup. The road was so bad we had to be flown in along with our groceries and my new helper's guitar. Vicky, my new helper, was an attractive woman in her early thirties. I had met Vicky the summer before when I went to a camp to relieve the cook. That camp was clean and tidy and the men liked her very much. Vicky played guitar very well and sometimes gave lessons to those who were serious about their music.

We arrived in camp in the early afternoon. I knew, when I checked our groceries, that we were in trouble. We didn't have any steaks or roasts, and we were missing a lot of other expensive items.

We cleaned up the kitchen that evening and were heading to our quarters when a man came down the hallway to meet us. He was tall and very good-looking, but he needed a shave. His hair was long and unruly and he looked like he had slept in his clothes — a speculation that proved to be true according to our campy. He hadn't been in the dining room for supper. The campy said he'd just landed in the chopper. In fact our campy told us quite a lot about this man who turned out to be our tool pusher. He said he drank a lot and spent most of his time in town. He said it was only a matter of time until the push was fired or sent to another rig. Our campy also warned us about the drillers on this camp. He said they all drank too — in camp and in the doghouse. When the driller drinks in camp, or on the job, his crew does likewise. They didn't want women like us in camp to change the way things were. They liked camp just fine the way it was before we were sent in to clean it up.

I knew we had been carefully chosen to go out to this job. We replaced a cook and helper who drank with the rig hands and didn't do a very good job in the meal department. I suspected the complaint had come from the oil company engineer or geologist.

The tool pusher walked into the kitchen just as we were leaving, never said who he was, and demanded that we go to town with him.

"Just for a few drinks, a dance or two, then home OK? We'll go in the chopper."

"I'm sorry . . . I just . . . I'm just too tired to go . . . but thanks anyway." I said.

"How about you, Vicky? You want to come along?"

"No thanks." She managed a grin.

By that time we realized this guy really was our tool push. And, he knew us both by name . . . curious!

"Well to hell with you two . . . bitches. It'll be the last time I ask!" He turned and slammed out of the kitchen. We heard him leave camp, and then we heard the chopper take off.

We went to our quarters and agreed that we would ask to be taken out as soon as possible. We walked down the hallway to the push's quarters or office and tried the door. It was locked. That room had the only mobile phone in camp. It was the first time I'd ever been on a rig camp when I, or anyone else, didn't have access to the mobile. I wondered if the campy had a key. We knocked on his door, but he wasn't in. He wasn't in the kitchen either, so we knew he was either in one of the rooms with the rig hands or out in one of the trailers at the rig.

We returned to our room and went to bed. I heard the chopper come in at about 3 a.m., and then there was a lot of noise in camp. It was not a very good place to be. I wanted out.

Not many rig hands came in for breakfast. There were a lot of snide remarks about the chopper coming in late, "Did you girls enjoy your trip to town?" I was furious. It was obvious the rig hands thought we'd gone to town with the tool push.

We cleaned up the breakfast mess and got lunch and dinner started. It was time to contact head office and ask to be taken out of that camp. I hated to go to the push's office, but I had to. I knocked several times and then waited. I was almost certain he was in his office. Then I heard a muffled, "Who's there?"

"Its me, Bev, the cook. I'd like to use the mobile, please."

"Just a minute." Then, after a three or four minute wait, he shouted for me to come in.

I certainly was not prepared for what was on the other side of that door. The push was sitting on his bunk — stark naked. His legs were spread open and his genitals hanging over the edge of the bed. He was scratching his head and smirking at me. I was dumb-founded. I stopped in my tracks and stared at him. I couldn't believe anyone would do that. But I recovered fast. I knew this was the only mobile in camp, and I had to use it to get out of the situation we were in. I stepped up to the phone, but my fingers wouldn't move right. My mind wasn't functioning properly. When I finally managed to dial, the line was busy.

The push got up off his bunk and walked over to where the mobile phone sat on his desk. My hands were shaking as I dialed the call numbers again, then the operator came on the line to say, "Your call cannot go through at this time. The lines are all busy."

I stood there with the receiver in my hand and turned to face Dennis. He grabbed the receiver out of my hand and said, "This call of yours . . . it's really important?"

"Yes," I said, looking him right in the eye.

"Well then, I'll just bump some stupid son-of-a-bitch off that line, so you can get through." He stood there grinning at me and handed me the receiver after he got through to head office in Edmonton. Then he walked across the room to where I couldn't help but see him. He was scratching his crotch and stretching, and I knew he was just waiting for me to get off the phone. It was obvious he hadn't shaved for several days. He was a disgusting mess.

I had to wait for several minutes before someone at head office answered the phone. There was a gruff hello.

"Hello, It's Bev. on Monteray 33. I want out of this camp. So does Vicky. As soon as possible, please."

And then Dennis grabbed the receiver from me. "Yeh, send someone in here who can cook . . . and be sociable." There was so much static on the line, I couldn't make out the rest of the conversation. Then Dennis smirked at me and handed the receiver back to me. "It's all yours."

There was no one on the line. I turned to leave the room, but Dennis was fast. He beat me to the door and stood right in front of me. Then he slowly opened the door and whispered a threat in my ear. I recoiled in horror at his words. "You'll be sorry about this . . . ."

I didn't cry until I had reached my quarters. I told Vicky what had happened. It left us in a real quandary. We still didn't know if or when, our replacements would be in, or when we could get out. We decided to go out to the rig lease as soon as the push left camp so that we could ask to use the geologist's mobile phone . . . or the engineer's. We had to get out somehow. I made plans in my mind. I would ask one of them to call in the chopper to take us out. I wasn't afraid . . . yet; I was disgusted. With this antagonistic attitude of the tool push and the drillers, I knew this camp was not a safe place for Vicky and I to be. There would be trouble.

The chopper left right after lunch. Dennis hadn't come into the kitchen for breakfast, so we weren't sure whether or not he was on the chopper. We took our chances and went out to the rig site anyway. We met the engineer on the lease, and he said he would be glad to let us use his mobile. He took us into his trailer and got our head office on the line. I knew he wanted to know who I was calling, so I left the key open so he could hear both sides of the conversation. I turned around to thank him. He sort of hung his head then said, "A sorry mess, up there . . . in camp. I sure was hoping you girls would stay and straighten it out. You both come with excellent credentials . . . I made it my business to know that. I'm sorry if I've offended you in any way, but we . . . they . . . your company, has a real mess up there in camp. I'm real sorry."

"So are we . . . actually. It's good to be working during spring breakup. But I won't stay in a camp like this. Even the drillers are drinking . . . I think. I'm quite sure the rig hands are too . . . No, we aren't staying. Its not safe. I know what happens in situations like this . . . the guys get drinking and . . . ."

"Would you girls consider staying if I pulled a few strings . . . at your head office?"

I was very surprised. I really didn't know what to say. I looked at Vicky and we both grinned. "Now wouldn't that be something! Wow! I don't know what to say. That's a real compliment. I don't know if we should . . . but then . . . uh. We'll talk it over, OK?"

I think the engineer knew we would stay if we had a decent push. Oil company engineers and geologists have been known to override drilling companies in the past. After all, the drilling company is hired by the oil company to drill the well. What a deal!

We decided to wait in camp for the engineer. We didn't have long to wait. He and the geologist walked into camp about two hours after we had left his trailer. They made us a deal we couldn't refuse. They assured us a new push would be in camp as soon as they could possibly get one. Actually, they said a new push would be on the next chopper flight — somewhere around supper time. They told us the present push's conduct would have forced them to do something anyway, but they were anxious for us to stay. "We know you can clean this place up and make it respectable again. And . . . uh . . . we've contacted you're supervisor, and he is very happy you've changed your mind about wanting out." I took that to be the ultimate compliment. So did Vicky.

They were going to let Dennis stay in Grande Cache as long as he wanted, but his chopper would not be available to him when he wanted to get back into camp.

I wondered how, or where, our head office people found and hired a new tool pusher in just a few hours. This was some sort of miracle! For once our head office had listened to a complaint. But then, they could hardly ignore it. The oil company is the ultimate boss out there in the field. We didn't care. We were used to our status in camp. We were definitely at the very bottom of the pecking order, but we had finally found someone who appreciated us.

The camp became a different place once that push was gone. The drillers changed their attitude and so did their men. None of them ever became real friendly, but we eventually did have a pretty good working arrangement. And there was no more drinking on the job or in camp. A camp is only as good as its pusher, and the new one turned out to be a real gem. But the engineer and geologist on that job went right to the top in our books.

That job turned out to be one of the best for both of us. We had a lot of fun, worked hard, and Vicky met a man who eventually became her husband. They were married on New Year's Day the following year. I helped move that camp to the next three wells for a total of 18 months. That is a long time to stay on one rig camp! But still no knight in shining armour ever arrived for me.

Chapter Seventeen

Accident

"SOMEONE GET ON THE MOBILE. Quick, tell anyone on it to get off the line." The driller's voice boomed down the hallway as he hurried to waken the rig hands who were on the other shift.

I heard the ruckus, grabbed my robe and slippers, and hurried down the hallway to find a rig hand, covered in mud, with three men working over him.

"What happened? Who is that?" I asked, almost afraid to know.

"Sandy. Its Sandy . . . He fell off the doghouse . . . and into the sump," offered Doug, the roughneck who was still pounding Sandy's back and listening to his shallow breathing.

It was about 35 degrees Fahrenheit below zero that night. I had been watching the temperature fall all evening; I thought that winter was here for sure. It was "tearing out" time prior to a rig move. This is always a very dangerous time for rig hands.

"Here, let me do it for awhile." The second roughneck put his head on Sandy's chest and then shouted. "He's not breathing. Come on Sandy . . . " Doug shoved the roughneck out of the way and started mouth-to-mouth resuscitation again. I couldn't help notice how muddy they all were. They must have been trying to make Sandy breath, or keep breathing, for a long time.

The motorman came out of the push's office. He shouted that he had got through and an ambulance was on its way.

"We'll go and meet it, OK?" Doug said to Rudy, the motorman.

"Sure, save a little time that way."

I watched those very young men as they went about the business of saving their buddy. I was quite sure every man on that crew was very glad he had completed the mandatory Industrial First Aid course we had taken on the previous well. It couldn't have happened at a better time. I shuddered as I remembered all the grumbling that went on about having to take it.

We all breathed a little easier when Sandy started choking and coughing. At least he was alive. They rolled him over on his side and slapped his back as they carried him out of camp and into the back of a truck that was used as a makeshift ambulance. It had a canopy with room for two stretchers and four crouching men. It was also heated, as there was no window between the back and the cab of the truck.

None of us who were left standing in that hallway knew if Sandy would live. We started to clean up the mud, and slowly the crew drifted back outside to continue the job of tearing out in the cold dark night.

Sandy, a derrickman, had been working on the roof of the doghouse. He slipped and fell into the frozen sump, breaking the ice. He'd been knocked out and was very lucky that Jeff, one of the two men working near him, had seen him fall. Jeff immediately climbed down, threw a chunk of plywood on the ice, and crawled out to rescue him — not an easy task considering the conditions.

Because he was unconscious and covered with drilling mud, it was very difficult to drag Sandy out. It was surely a miracle that anyone had seen him fall because it was a very dark night. Even if he hadn't been unconscious, the noise from the motors was so loud that a call for help would never have been heard, even by someone working nearby.

That morning took a long time to come. We all watched the road and listened for the horn on the mobile. We wanted desperately to know how Sandy was. If he . . . .

At about 10 a.m., the rig hands returned. Sandy was OK. He had some broken ribs and a broken wrist, but, after nearly choking to death, he was breathing. He was kept in the hospital, because the doctor was worried that the residue in his lungs would cause infection.

Sandy suffered a lot of setbacks. He developed pneumonia, then went into a severe depression, and finally had a nervous breakdown. He stayed home for a long time.

Another derrickman had been hired, but the push had reassured Sandy the job was his as soon as he was ready to return to the rig. When we heard he had been released from hospital, we looked for him at every long change. Eventually he did show up but not for long.

He drove into camp, changed his clothes and put in less than an hour on the job. Then he just left the rig. He came into camp, gathered up his gear, got into his truck, and drove away. We never saw him again.

Much later, we heard Sandy had attended the school of agriculture in Olds, Alberta. Sometime later he took over the family farm. He was not coming back to our rig, or any rig, ever again.

Chapter Eighteen

Pete

I had been working with a very young push who was good with his men and good about getting our food orders for the camp. I had been in some camps where the good roasts and steaks never arrived — they went directly from the grocery store into the push's truck. With Dale it was good. We could order anything, and be assured it would be in camp as soon as he could possibly get it there. It was during the height of the boom years, when experienced rig hands were hard to come by — especially good ones. We were drilling a well in bush country . . . not far out of Fox Creek.

Our push, Dale, went out on long change and we didn't know who would be taking his place. Over the previous six months we had had seven different relief pushes. About an hour after Dale left camp, a man arrived and announced he was the relief push. He was an older man of about fifty-five, with astonishing blue eyes. He was quite good-looking but seemed very shy. He wrote his name down on the meal sheet and, after drinking a cup of coffee and exchanging small talk about the state of the roads, left for the rig.

A roughneck appeared at the back door asking for the fresh doughnuts that I'd promised would be ready at coffee time. "See our new push?"

"Yeah. Seems like an okay guy," I said.

"Wait 'til he's around for a day or two. Worst old bastard in the oil patch. Don't know where they dragged him out of . . . I thought he was still in the nut house. He's been run off every rig in Alberta."

My goodness. I reprimanded the roughneck on his manners and told him he should have more respect for his elders. It was a reprimand that I was to revoke in a very short time.

The days slipped by, and before we knew it, long change was about to take place again. We'd played cards with our new push and spent many hours telling lies around the lunch table. We were convinced he was a nice guy and ignored all the warnings from the rig hands who knew him. We should have taken heed of the lack of humour or teasing when Pete, our relief push, was around. The men disliked him intensely, and I often wondered about that roughneck's remark about the nut house.

The evening before he was to go out, I suspected Pete was drinking, but he didn't stick around the dining room very long. He left right after breakfast, and Dale arrived shortly thereafter. When Dale walked into camp, he was grinning as usual, but my helper and I knew he had something on his mind. Before he left for the rig, he asked us how we had got along with Pete while he was gone.

"Fine. Seemed like a nice guy."

"He didn't get into the booze then?"

"Not that we know of."

"That's good. He goes a little squirrely when he's drinking. Probably quit by now. He used to be one of the best pushes in the business." Dale left us to mull over that statement. It was soon forgotten.

A month later Pete was back to relieve Dale again. He was sober when he arrived but was drunk within the hour. He came down the hall from his office, sat down at the table and began shuffling cards. "How's about a game of gin, Bev?" he asked.

"I'm pretty busy Pete. It's pretty early for that anyway," I said as I got up from the table with intentions of going back into the kitchen. He grabbed my hand and pulled me back down into my chair. I spilled my plate of half-eaten bacon and eggs and slopped my coffee all over the place. I pulled my hand away and made another attempt at leaving. Pete slammed the cards down and shouted at me.

"Well, damn the work. When I want someone to play gin with me, I want them to play gin right away." He came around the table. I knocked over a couple of chairs but I got away and ran into the kitchen with Pete right behind me. I was shocked to think he would do such a thing. I dropped my plate on a cupboard and ran out the door into the hallway and across to my quarters where I immediately locked myself in. My helper was in her room housecleaning. She came through the adjoining doors and asked what was wrong. When I told her Pete was after me, she almost laughed. "You're kidding!"

"No, I'm not. The old fool is drunk . . . at this time of the day!" I was still shaking.

We listened for some time and eventually heard him drive off the camp lease. We ran to the kitchen window to make sure he had gone to the rig. He had.

We didn't see him for the rest of that day. He must have gone into the kitchen to make himself something to eat that evening after we'd gone to bed. There was no sign of him at the breakfast table, and the night crew told us he hadn't shown up all night at the rig. Pete avoided us for the next two days. We saw him leave camp and drive toward the rig, but he never came near us. On the fifth day he walked in for breakfast as though nothing had happened. He was cheerful and talkative. There was a noticeable hush around the table until he left for the rig. The rig hands said he was right on the ball all that day, but the following day he began drinking again. The driller told us, before he went out for the graveyard shift, to watch Pete. He was terribly drunk in his office. The driller had gone in to use the mobile and Pete had been stretched out, dead drunk, on his bunk.

Just as we were nearly finished our day's work and were leaving the kitchen, Pete appeared in the doorway with a bottle. He pushed past my helper and slammed the bottle down hard on the table.

"Get a couple of glasses there, sweety. You girls are gonna have a little smash with this old tooly before he goes out in the morning." He was stumbling over chairs and bumping into the table.

"Go back to your office, Pete. You're drunk," I said.

"Now just who in the hell do you think you are anyway. Telling me what to do!"

Carol and I kept edging our way toward the door to make a hasty escape. He darted toward the door and beat us to the punch. "Now you girls look here a minute. When I say I'm gonna have a little drink with someone, they always have a drink with me." He was waving the bottle around dangerously. I knew the day shift had gone to town, and I knew the campy was out at the engineer's trailer playing gin rummy. We were the only people in camp at that time.

Pete turned and started down the hall to his office. He turned around and said, "Come on girls. Won't take very long." We watched until he was nearly at his door and then started running. Carol had boots on. I was wearing house shoes. We grabbed a couple of jackets hanging at the door and ran for the rig. We were halfway there when we heard Pete's truck start up and pull onto the road. I knew I couldn't run all the way to the rig with slippery house shoes on, so I shouted to Carol to keep going. I jumped into the snow bank and climbed across the debris left when they bulldozed the road through. To this day I don't know how I got over that mountain of brush and trees. I crouched down low so he couldn't see me. I held my breath as he drove past on his way to try and overtake Carol.

I could hear Carol screaming for help as she ran. I knew it was useless because of the noise from the rig motors. Pete was right behind her when she ran up the long stairs to the doghouse where the crew was working. A roughneck who was walking across the lease spotted her and then saw Pete step down from the stairs and get back into his truck. Carol was near tears and very upset. The whole crew listened to her story and decided that one or two of the men would go back down to camp and try to get Pete into a safe place for the rest of the night. The driller assigned one roughneck and the derrickman to go back with Carol in another truck. They picked me up along the way. I was wet and cold and terribly frightened.

We had a short conference about what we were going to do. Brent, the derrickman, said he'd stay in camp with us. He sent the roughneck out to the rig to get the campy and to inform the engineer about what was taking place in camp. We cautioned him on that score, and it was decided not to tell the engineer. The engineer worked for the oil company, and we worked for the drilling company. Generally, on the oil rigs, it was considered better to keep one's dirty laundry to oneself. We decided to ask the forklift operator to help instead.

The roughneck arrived with the campy, who was half drunk himself. I showed Brent the lock on our door; I knew it wouldn't hold if Pete tried to get in. Brent went down the hallway examining every door to see if there was one safe room where we could spend the night. The campy's room was the only place. Old Scotty had a lock on that door that would keep anyone out.

Carol and I brought our night clothes to Scotty's room, and we could hear Brent shouting at Scotty. "You get your ass down there to the girls' quarters and sleep it off . . . and stay out of the way for the rest of the night. If Pete tries to get into that room, start yelling. Don't you let him in there, and don't start drinking with him again."

We couldn't sleep. We heard the crew come in around midnight and go to their rooms. We must have drifted off to sleep after that, because we were awakened by the sound of someone chopping. We sure came to our senses when we saw the blade of an axe come through that flimsy door. We started screaming and watched in horror as the blade made another appearance. And then we heard someone running.

There was a lot of noise outside the door, but we just kept on screaming and yelling. Finally in our panic we heard Brent say that everything was all right. It was some time before we got up enough courage to open what was left of that door. We were both crying and very close to hysteria. We did calm down when the rig hands assured us Pete was on his way to the mud shack where he would stay, under lock and key, until other arrangements were made.

There wasn't much point in going back to bed. It was nearly 5 a.m., so we showered and went to work. We were assured that Pete wouldn't be allowed to enter camp unattended. He would soon be out of our lives for good.

When Dale arrived, he went straight to the rig. We learned later he'd met Pete on the way in, and Pete told him he'd made a complete fool of himself. When Dale finally got brave enough to come into camp, he was full of apologies.

"'I'm sorry, Bev. I know I shoulda told you what a stupid bastard Pete is when he's drinking . . . ."

"If you knew what a jerk he was, why did you, or the office, hire him back in the first place?"

"Short of men. I'm real sorry for what happened. He used to be a good man."

"Why does the office keep taking him back?"

It was a good question, but in those days it was hard to get experienced men, and I assume Pete told the company brass that he'd quit drinking.

I considered reporting this incident to head office, but knew that no one there would have taken us seriously. This was still very much a "good old boys" industry, and it would be a long time before women were treated with any kind of respect on the rigs.

That was the only time I was ever really afraid on the rigs. I learned, much later, that Pete was suffering from a mental disorder and didn't understand the importance of taking his medication on a regular basis. I also learned that our encounter with him was not an isolated incident. I heard from a reliable source that, under court order, Pete had been sent to an Alberta hospital for a mental assessment. A woman he was living with had charged him with several counts of assault. She was a nurse and knew Pete had to take his medication. I thought she must have cared for him a great deal to have had enough courage to take him to court so that something would be done.

Other rig cooks were not so lucky.

An oil worker was accused of raping a rig cook, but he testified in court that the cook had consented to the incident. The forty-year-old engineer said he and the woman had been leaving camp on long change. He testified that he had stopped to see that all his co-workers had made it out safely because the road was so muddy. While they waited the two had drunk whisky and had begun petting and kissing. Then they had driven to a more secluded spot and had had sex.

The engineer said that he had not raped the woman. He went to trial before Mr. Justice J.A. Agrios and a three-woman, nine-man court of Queen's Bench jury. He denied holding a knife to the cook's throat and forcing her to have sex. He told the court that they had resumed their trip out of camp and that the cook had started complaining that he was driving too fast. He said he had been having trouble keeping the truck on the road because it was so slippery, and, eventually, they had slipped into the ditch and had become stuck in the muskeg. He said he had tried, unsuccessfully, to drive out. He had then decided to wait for a vehicle to come along and pull him out.

He said the woman had been very angry and had insisted that he do something. The engineer had said there was nothing he could do; they were stuck. They had argued, and he had told her to walk if she didn't want to wait. She told the court that she had walked for some time but had eventually returned to the truck. A trucker hauling a load to another camp had come along and had agreed to pull them out of the ditch on his return trip. When the arrangements had been completed, the engineer had returned to his truck and had locked the woman out of it. He had said it was to teach her a lesson. The woman had managed to chase down the trucker and ride with him.

The engineer said that was the last he saw of the woman.

The woman told the court the engineer had given her an ultimatum — either walk or come across. She said she had submitted to having sex with the man because he had threatened her with a knife.

I didn't hear the outcome of that trial because I was assigned to a rig so far out in the bush we seldom got a newspaper.

Shortly after the Christmas holidays that year, our push took us for an outing over to a neighbouring rig to exchange movies. There was a terrible mix up in that camp — real chaos. The regular tool push was out on his long change, and the relief push had got mixed up with the three relief camp crew — all women. A cat skinner, who was cleaning up the camp after the party the previous evening, told us it was quite a mess. He said he had arrived just in time to see the RCMP haul away the relief push and three rig hands. The cooks and their female camp attendant had driven themselves out after they were raped in the rec trailer during the drinking party.

It is my firm belief that a rig camp is only as good as the man pushing the operation. If one is fortunate enough to work with a good tool push, then it's easy to maintain law and order if you have someone in authority to back you up. It's a foolish cook who doesn't keep her nose clean in a rig camp. A reputation spreads quickly, and, as in most industries, the boss is always right — even if he's wrong.

In spite of the incidents described in this chapter, we did meet some very nice men. Two of my helpers met the men they eventually married. I met the man I would fall in love with and would have married, but he was already married. I still haven't met a man I liked better or admired as much.

Chapter Nineteen

Traitors, Thieves and Scoundrels in the Oil Patch

AS IN MOST INDUSTRIES, there are traitors, thieves and scoundrels in the oil patch.

Oil patch scouting is the common term for the exchange of oil patch information. It usually occurs when a drilling company is working on an exploration well in new territory or when a land sale is in the offing. Oil companies will bid huge sums of money for rights to drill where they know the possibility of oil is greater.

Scouting is an accepted practice in the oil patch. The largest exchange of information is done in a sophisticated manner from posh hotel suites in major western Canadian oil cities.

However, there is another method of scouting — sometimes legal and sometimes not so legal. There is still a lot of information to be gained through the old-fashioned method of setting up camp just outside lease boundaries, where the scout can watch the drilling operation through binoculars. He monitors vehicles coming into camp, and, if he is as thorough as he probably told the oil company he's working for, he identifies every expert who comes onto the lease. He also determines just how deep the drilling is by counting the stands of pipe as they are brought out of the hole during a trip.

When I arrived on the oil patch, there were still a lot of scouts in the field. Somehow, I got the impression it was not a very respectable profession.

I know one driller who was suffering from the 26 ounce flu and had to trip as soon as he got on shift. The testers were in camp waiting, and the pressure of having these high-priced men in camp was not exactly what the driller was prepared for that morning. When the push arrived after breakfast and asked the driller where he was, meaning how many stands to go, he mumbled something he knew the push couldn't hear and worked hard at looking terribly busy. When he saw the push drive off the lease, the driller stepped out of the doghouse and looked over at the scout who was watching the driller through his binoculars.

The driller knew he had to grovel to get the information he needed. He climbed down the steps, walked over to the edge of the lease and lit a smoke very casually. He tried hard not to look in the direction of the scout. He kicked a clump of dirt around until the scout put the binoculars down and waved to him. The two had worked on the same rig on several occasions, but the driller, like a lot of rig hands, just couldn't forgive his old friend for taking a scouting job. However he knew he had to have an accurate count, and the scout was the only person who would have it. His whole crew was suffering from the same malady.

He scrambled over the piles of muskeg and bush at the edge of the lease and yelled at the scout, "Where am I?"

"Twenty-seven to go," the scout replied.

"Thanks. I owe you one." The driller waved and headed back to his brake and continued tripping. It probably never crossed his mind how he was going to repay the scout.

When I worked on the second rig camp to drill a well in the "new" field at Beaverlodge, Alberta, scouts followed us around in droves. Toward the end of the first hole, we had nine scouts trailing us all — everywhere. We were followed into town, where they would select a table near enough to ours to be able to listen to our conversation. They would send drinks over to our table and ask to sit with us when my helper and I went into town early to shop. On these special occasions, when we were drilling so close to civilization, my helper and I would go to the bar or lounge and secure a table for our crew who would drive in when their shift was over at 8 p.m.

Scouts know cooks have access to information about who's in camp and how the drilling is progressing, because most of us answered the mobile when the push was not in camp. I never worried much about letting out information, as most rig personnel thought the cooks didn't know very much anyway.

But we did have a bit of fun with two particularly persistent scouts one afternoon. To avoid suspicion we filled two pails with fresh cookies and headed out to the rig to have coffee with the guys. It was not an everyday practice, but on occasion when we were bored, we would go out to the doghouse to make fun of their messy lunchroom and to let the driller show us how clever he was. If we were lucky, he might let us handle the stick for a minute or two just so we could brag about being able to drill.

The roughneck who came into camp for coffee and goodies was escorting us, and we supposed the scouts were watching us as we handed over one pail of cookies. We spent about a half-hour with the crew and then headed toward the scouts' camp. As we approached the edge of the lease, one came to meet us.

"Hi! Thought you guys might like a few fresh cookies. Must be pretty boring out here for you guys." We smiled our most glamorous smiles.

"Gee, thanks. Come on over and have coffee with us."

"We just had coffee with the crew. Gotta get back to work. Enjoy the cookies." We headed back to camp while the two scouts dug into the fresh batch of cookies. They had no idea they were laced with Exlax. Earlier, we had told our crew what we'd done. They were hesitant to eat their cookies, but we had reassured them that we had kept our cookie batches straight.

We heard later that the two scouts were kept pretty busy for a day or two and couldn't spend all their time watching through binoculars.

The last rig camp I worked at was about fifty-six miles from Grande Cache. A rig, drilling a hole a few miles from our lease, had a rich strike. There was a great deal of speculation about ours, so the engineer and tool push couldn't give their reports on the mobile telephone but had to drive several miles each day to use the nearest land phone. This was a pay phone which was located on an abandoned service station lot at Little Muskeg. At that time, it was probably one of the busiest phones in northern Alberta.

All through that fall, the push would drive to Little Muskeg to give his report. As the drilling progressed and the roads got increasingly worse, he and the engineer would drive out together. Because my helper and I were so bored, they asked us to go along for the drive one evening.

As we approached the old lot, we saw the trucks lined up waiting to use the pay phone. Our superiors chatted about rig problems, poor help, the fall of Joe Clark's government, and bored cooks. There was never a word about how the drilling was progressing. They weren't about to discuss that with the cooks. That information was for head office only. They had no idea of our knowledge of what was taking place on the drill site. We probably knew as much as any roughneck on the drill platform, but none of the brass would admit that. After all, cooks were women. They were sure women didn't know a thing about rigs or drilling.

A few days after that particular trip, an engineer from a neighbouring rig drove into camp one night and asked if the push was around. He poured himself a cup of coffee and sat down to chat until the push finished his conversation on the mobile phone.

Woody came across from his office and smiled at his visitor. "Hi Frank. What's new?"

"You know that pay phone at Little Muskeg?"

"Yeah."

"Well . . . it's bugged. God damned scout must have got . . . all kinds of information . . . ."

"No shit. How'd you find out?"

"Oh . . . another guy told me this morning. Said he was talking to the engineer, Mel, and another fellow . . . from that rig drillin' down in that valley where the fuel truck turned over. Said that engineer was waiting to get through . . . kicked an old coke can and . . . The snow melted a lot in that last Chinook you know . . . . He saw the wire leading out of the booth and went out to investigate. God damned tape recorder set up. Probably got every word we've been sending in for a month or two."

"Did he get the recorder?"

"No. The scout left the box he had it in though. It's as plain as day. It had to be a tape recorder. The guy who was doing it must have left in a hurry when he saw someone coming."

No doubt there were a lot of very confused oil executives receiving calls at that time.

There was another type of theft making an appearance in Canada about the time I left the rigs: theft of oil patch data. This crime is just not tolerated in Canada.

The act of gathering of oil patch data is called well logging. The information is collected with special logging tools using electrical, radioactive, sonic, and other methods of down hole analysis. This information is meant for oil company personnel only. The results of this well logging is extremely confidential if the exploration is being carried out in a "wildcat" area or a new field of exploration. Well logging is an expensive procedure, and the oil company footing this huge bill isn't about to share the information with another company.

Oil company personnel are usually the only people on the drilling rig when well logging takes place. The driller is present, but his crew is probably performing cleaning and maintenance duties while the logging is taking place. Well logging is performed by highly trained specialists employed by a wireline well logging company. Samples of core and/or rock are taken for analysis. The oil company must have complete faith in the "testing" or logging company and in its employees.

However, in 1980, one well logging employee, Norman Straden, a 27-year-old employee of one of the top wireline companies in the world, Schlumberger Canada, thought he might take advantage of the logging information taken from a test well in the Grande Prairie area. It turned out to be a serious mistake.

This was thought to be the first oil espionage conviction in a province where "oil spies" pursue an accepted profession. However, oil patch spying is one thing; outright theft of information is quite another.

Stranden had been working as a wireline operator on a well southeast of Grande Prairie, Alberta. He was performing exploration tests for Ocelot Industries of Canada. Witnesses told the court that Ocelot had spent $900,000 developing the well and was paying $32,000 for the test data to pinpoint the well's oil and gas potential. In addition, the company was planning to bid on adjacent lands and had declared the well in question a tight hole — a signal that it was not prepared to share any information about it with the rest of the industry.

Stranden very boldly announced an offer to sell six charts of detailed Ocelot information, and three rolls of film, to Gulf, Amoco and Dome Petroleum. The three companies took action immediately. Daniel Mulvenna, Dome's security chief at the time, was dispatched to

Edson with $25,000 in marked bills. He posed as interested oil scout. The exchange of half the information, in return for the cash, took place at Edson Sundowner Motel. Mulvenna agreed to bring an additional $25,000 for the rest of the information.

As Stranden walked out of the motel, three RCMP officers from the Edson detachment arrested him. He was sentenced to an eighteen-month prison term for the theft of oil well data. Mr. Justice A.W. Crossley of Queen's Bench ruled the stiff sentence in an effort to deter anyone else from trying such a theft. Crossley said the court must protect the legitimate pursuit of one of the province's most important natural resources. He hoped the Stranden sentence would stand as a strong deterrent.

Another man was arrested in Grande Prairie in a similar case when he was charged and convicted with theft of information on a Dome well site near Fort St. John, B.C. The courts gave him one year.

Oil patch information is not all that is stolen. A lot of thefts are done by rig hands who have been run off a rig or who have quit after they got to know the habits of the push and crews.

When a rig is racked, it is full of groceries, and the various trailers and shacks out at the drilling lease contain thousands of dollars worth of tools. It's a gold mine as far as thieves are concerned.

It is common to rack a rig and camp while waiting for a new lease to become ready or while waiting for spring breakup. That is also a time when a lot of rig workers take holidays. When a rig is racked, at least two people have to be in to "camp watch." One of these people must be able to operate the light plant. Usually a motorman, or someone higher up the ladder, stays with a roughneck. Sometimes the complete camp staff stays in camp, as the campy is usually an old rig hand or has been around camps long enough to be able to service the power plant.

It is an incredibly boring job. The camp watchers must guard the rig and camp trailers and monitor vehicles coming or going. The mobile is usually left operating, and at least one vehicle is left in camp for emergency purposes. The people left in camp are not supposed to leave camp and must mobile a daily report. They are supposed to be on duty 24 hours a day, in 12 hour shifts. If the camp is racked in an isolated area, there is usually not too much to worry about. After a day's watch is over, it is a time to fish or hunt and to watch TV.

One day, I was driving into our camp, which had been moved onto a new location while I was out on long change. Another of our company's rigs and camp, in the same area, was racked while waiting for a lease to become ready. I had been driving for over an hour when I saw one of our company trucks approaching me. We were both driving very slow, so by the time he was close I knew it was our "colors." I slowed down assuming the push would do the same and perhaps stop and tell me how the road was further in. I had a nodding acquaintance with most pushes in that area and was surprised when he didn't even slow down. The windshield was very muddy, and I couldn't make out who was driving the truck. I continued on, wondering about the snotty bastard who wouldn't even stop to say hello.

I had missed the rig move, and, as always, head office didn't give me very good directions into camp. I couldn't see any company signs or flags, but every time I came to a cut line trail I stopped and walked around in the ditches and roadways to see if one of our signs had been knocked over. As I picked my way around the third survey cut, I found our sign in muskeg, so I propped it up again. I still had another ten miles to go. Then I heard someone yelling at me. "Hello, hello, hello there."

Now, when you've been driving for an hour out on a bush road and haven't seen a soul, it's a strange sound to hear someone calling . . . especially without a vehicle in sight. I looked all around and finally saw two men running out of the bush toward me. I hurried into my truck, locked the door and had the window rolled up when the two men approached. I recognized one of them. He was a rig hand from the neighbouring rig, which I knew was racked. I felt more at ease, rolled down the window, and asked them where they came from.

"Camp. We're watching the camp. Well . . . supposed to. Haven't done a very good job though. Someone just drove off with just about everything." He was still puffing from his long run through the bush.

"Where's your truck? How come you guys are on foot?" I asked.

"Stole the truck too. Just about cleaned the whole camp out. Probably cleaned out the tools too, but we didn't go out to the rig site to find out. Pulled out the wires on the mobile too. Sure left us in a hell of a fix."

He looked my truck over. "You're the cook over on the other Baldwin rig aren't you? They just moved onto their new lease last week."

"Yes, I am the cook, and yes, it's a new hole," I said.

"Did you meet a company truck down the road awhile back?" He seemed very anxious. "Should have been another vehicle about the same time."

"Well, yes . . . I can't remember how far back . . . or if there was a second vehicle, but I'm sure it was a company truck. Can't mistake that shade of green." Then I remembered how unusual it was that the driver didn't stop. "Oh yeah. I remember now. It was right at that old sawmill location and there was another vehicle. It was quite a big truck with a tarp on it. That's right . . . . I wondered why the push didn't return my wave. I thought he was probably someone new. Didn't even stop to tell me about the road like a decent fellow would."

"Son-of-a-bitch. That's gotta be at least a half-hour ago, right?" The motorman was kicking mud off his boots. It seemed like he was avoiding my eyes. Both men were more than a little embarrassed.

"Been in here over three weeks and left the God damned camp for the first time today . . . to fish. Right behind the damned camp too. That bastard cleaned out camp as slick as a whistle. Even took the deep freezers for Christ sake."

"You don't suppose we could get you to drive us back to Fox Creek to see if we could overtake them or at least phone the RCMP?"

"How much further is the lease I'm trying to get to? The superintendent in head office said it's about forty miles off Highway 43, but I've gone forty-five miles now."

"Oh, it's about another five or six miles I think. I talked to one of the drivers when they were moving in.

Said the road's a bloody mess, and it's rained every day since then."

I sat there wondering what I should do. If the road was as bad as these guys said it was, then I probably couldn't drive all the way in anyway. I was quite sure the relief cooks wouldn't leave until I arrived, but they had the rig and camp move to contend with and would be pretty anxious about getting out. On the other hand . . . it was quite possible we could overtake the trucks . . . they would be travelling slower than us . . . .

"Okay, let's go. One of you guys want to drive?" I moved over. One fellow got in on each side, and we were off in a splash of mud.

I sat between them listening to their sad tale of woe. I'd spent time doing camp watch when the cooks had to clean up a kitchen after it had been turned over en route. I knew how boring it could be, but a job's a job. They should have stayed right in camp, and they both knew it.

We arrived in Fox Creek without overtaking the two trucks. We telephoned the RCMP with the information we had. Then we phoned our head office. When the shouting let up on the superintendents line, I asked to speak to him so he could mobile my push and tell him why I didn't arrive as scheduled. I had to let him know where I was.

My push agreed to bring the relief cooks out to Fox Creek the following morning. He advised me to take one of the motel rooms in Fox Creek that our company reserved year round. I was to wait for him there. He said the road into our new lease was too muddy. "You'd never make it in here with your little pickup. Stay put 'til I come to fetch you, OK?" In situations like that the push would be using a four by four heavy duty pick-up truck equipped with a winch and could, in all likelihood, get through almost any mud hole.

The company truck was found abandoned along Highway 43, but the tools and groceries were never located. Quite a few people were suspect and to my knowledge no one was arrested in that particular incident.

A driller had been run off that rig some time earlier, and later that fall all our vehicles were broken into when they were parked about a half-mile from camp. As in all thefts someone has to be blamed, so everyone blamed the driller who was run off, and stories began to circulate about his unusual behaviour while he was on our rig.

Chapter Twenty

Tight Hole

YOU MAY HAVE HEARD the expression "tight hole" on a news broadcast or read it in a newspaper article and wondered what it meant. Some of the reasons why the company brass determine a well should be a tight hole, are mentioned in the previous chapter. However, there are a lot of other reasons why the signs are posted: signs of a huge oil strike, a land sale coming up in the area, a cave-in . . . .

When the decision is made, signs will be put up on the main road leading to a rig site, then on a turn-off road, and again at all the trails leading from that road right up to the edge of the camp lease. A trucker with a load to deliver to a tight hole lease will have to get permission from the engineer, geologist or tool push before he is allowed to go past camp. If anyone else is stupid enough to drive beyond camp without permission, it is at his own risk.

One time, our engineer put a tight hole sign up when we had a Christmas party in camp. He didn't want any rig hands coming over from another rig and crashing our party. At least that's what he told us. Drilling was completed and some service personnel and wireline logging specialists were already in camp. Thus there was a legitimate excuse for the tight hole warning signs.

Earlier that fall, I had been having problems keeping a helper. My helper for the previous two years had gone back to school. I went through a raft of girls. Some I knew would never last on a rig camp and others I just didn't have time to train. I was becoming very short-tempered.

Then I thought about my daughter-in-law, Pat, whose sister, Cindy, had often mentioned she would like to give it a try. I mobiled Pat and my son Doug from our push's mobile, but our connection was poor. I signed off saying I'd phone from camp after I'd talked to my push. Pat told me Cindy was home again from Montreal where she had been attending university. She said Cindy was not ready to settle into a job yet and would very likely want to try the position — for a short time anyway.

I phoned Cindy right after I'd fired the third girl in a week. Cindy agreed to come for a short time. Pat told her it would be an "experience" she wouldn't forget. Pat knew what she was talking about, as Pat, and my second son Doug, had gone out to a job with me on one occasion when they wanted to save some money. They both decided the isolation and camp life was not what they were looking for and went on to different careers.

Cindy just happened to be very beautiful, and as soon as she hit camp she was the center of attention. She had help doing the dishes and peeling vegetables, and someone always carried the heavy coffee urn from the kitchen to the dining room for her. She was invited to go to town with every rig hand who had a vehicle in camp. Within a week she had five proposals of marriage — two from guys who offered to divorce their wives as soon as she gave them the word — and three other offers of co-habitation.

Cindy was too smart to play favourites in that situation. She played cards with them all, smiled at them all, and refused all invitations and offers. When she entered a room every man in it dashed to offer her the best chair available. It was hilarious to watch. Cindy was suitably impressed. She was enjoying her "experience."

We were both slated to stay in camp over Christmas and New Years. This extra pay suited Cindy as she was saving money for a trip to Hawaii.

I had been on that camp for a long time and knew the crews and the push well. It was a deep hole rig and we had a prince of an engineer, a very nice geologist, and a great tool push aboard. All three of the brass hovered over us while we prepared for a little Christmas Eve party, and I was grateful when the engineer and geologist offered to help. I admired our push for allowing us to have the small party. Most of the rig hands were in camp, since there were testers in camp, and being in camp over a holiday, especially Christmas, is not usually much fun.

It was late when we were finished in the kitchen that night. There were a lot of men in camp, and more would be in through the night. The end of a hole, with all the extra people around, is a trying time for cooks. Just before I left the kitchen to shower and dress for the evening, I ground up a large bowl of bread crumbs to use in the turkey stuffing the following morning.

When I entered the recreation trailer I was glad to hear the laughter. I didn't want it to be a sad party. There were quite a few guys in camp who were married and had young families. I always tried to make the best of a holiday, but this seemed to outdo anything I'd ever planned before. Cindy was the main attraction. She was an excellent hostess and fun to be around. She had that special magic. The guys forgot everything and enjoyed themselves. By that time at least five guys were madly in love with her.

We played cards, stuffed ourselves with goodies, and told lies until it was time to go to bed. Nearly everyone had a few drinks, but one roughneck got out of hand. He was drunk. I was very surprised at this. Our brass had been very careful with the drinks. I realized he must have been drinking in his room before he came to the party. That was not going to be tolerated.

When the drunk roughneck started shouting and shoving guys around, we all knew there would be trouble. Someone had to stop him. A fight can get out of hand so easily when people are drinking. The roughneck's driller got up, knocked the roughy off his chair, and escorted him to his room. As soon as the driller returned to the party, the roughy came back too. He started his shouting all over again. He was even more aggressive this time. The main reason the roughneck was arguing was he thought someone else was taking up too much of Cindy's time. She had turned down a game of gin with him earlier because he was too drunk, and she told him so — point blank.

The tool push was engrossed in a game of gin with Cindy and didn't want to be disturbed, so he told the crew to "throw that bastard in the snow bank 'till he cools off. I'll see he won't come back in here."

We shut the party down when they escorted the roughy to his room the second time. I retired to my room and I heard Cindy go into her room shortly after. I heard the testers come into camp and then go into the kitchen where we'd left food out for them. The testers had called in more equipment. I was quite curious about all these extra service hands they kept calling in. I wasn't surprised when I overheard the engineer and push talking, at the party, about a possible gusher.

I fell asleep wondering how we were going to get through the next week or ten days. We already had so many men in camp. I drifted off to sleep but woke when I heard a loud noise in the kitchen. Someone was banging on pots and yelling and singing. I wondered what was going on. I looked at my watch. It was 4 a.m. — too early to get up. Then I heard another round of laughter, a few crashes, and more yelling. It was too loud to ignore. I didn't want them to get into my Christmas baking, and I didn't want them to break anything. I had to get up.

Cindy came into my room as I was putting my housecoat on. We walked quietly across the hall and looked in through the kitchen window. They had closed the hall door so we wouldn't hear them I guess.

It was a sight I will never forget!

Two men from one of our crews were walking slowly down the center of the room between the tables, arm in arm. One had a towel over his head which, I assume, was supposed to be a veil. Another roughneck was pounding out a lot of noise on a tin pot with two large spoons. The rest of our rig hands were lined up, hanging onto each other, and singing as loud as they could. I believe they were trying to sing the wedding march . . . but in gee-how-flat.

There wasn't a sober man in that room. They were having a ball. It was a scream!

Then one fellow said, "I know this isn't CCCCCCindy. Oh Cindy . . . where are you? . . . But it's the best we can do."

Then one of the service hands, dressed in his coveralls, his hard hat and a towel around his neck — backwards, to resemble a minister . . . I think — said, "I pronounce you guys man and wife . . . or man . . . and . . . man . . . no wife." He had one of my cook books open and was solemnly reading a recipe for butter tarts.

After the "I dos" were completed, one of the guys grabbed my bread crumbs and tossed them over everyone. There was a great roar of laughter. It was hilarious, but . . . .

It was time to interfere. It was so funny I couldn't stop laughing. There were apologies from all over the room. Then they offered to clean up the mess.

When we returned to the kitchen there wasn't a bread crumb around, and everything was put back in its proper place. It had been quite an evening.

There were a lot of hung-over rig hands and service men the next day who dragged themselves into the dining room for Christmas dinner. Every time we'd look at the guys involved in the wedding performance, we'd all start laughing. It wasn't such a sad Christmas that year after all.

Cindy left at the end of that well and went on to become a journalist. She worked for a major newspaper in Edmonton for some time before leaving for Europe where she lived for a short time. Cindy has returned to Canada, and she and Pat were a great help in editing this book. They both grinned and chuckled a lot as they edited.

Cindy made a terrific impression on everyone in that camp. She was talked about for months, until I got another helper who was just about as beautiful and who also knew how to conduct her life in camp — not an easy task.

Our push removed the tight hole sign when we pulled out of that camp. To this day I don't know whether we had a gusher or a dry well.

I left the rigs for good shortly after that well. I went back to writing — this time at *The Edson Leader* in my home town of Edson, Alberta. I stayed for a year. I had quietly written many notes and stories while I was still on the rigs. I knew I would eventually write a book about the oil rig camps, but an offer of a better job, in a larger newspaper, came along, and I left Alberta for North Battleford, Saskatchewan.

It was a long way from the B.C.-Alberta oil patch. I was astonished to realize how little my co-workers in Saskatchewan knew about the oil industry or about the people who worked in it.

We were all working at our computers in the newsroom one day when our editor looked up from his console. He was watching the wire service on his screen when suddenly he asked, "Ever hear of a tight hole, Bev?"

Our editor knew I was from Alberta, and I assume that was why he directed the question at me. He was from Ontario and knew nothing about the industry that was spewing out stories of blow-outs, sour gas leaks, oil well fires and accidents.

I looked across the newsroom at him and said, "Yes, of course I have. Why? What's happening? Oh . . . I'll bet it's that blowout at Lodgepole. I heard about it on the radio at noon."

I could see several reporters grinning. I knew they had never heard of a tight hole in the oil business. They didn't know what to say, and it was obvious that both of the women reporters were embarrassed about the expression "tight hole." None of my co-workers knew I'd worked in the oil patch before going to work on that newspaper.

I spent the rest of that afternoon explaining what a tight hole was to four reporters, two typesetters, and my editor. They were very surprised and impressed at my knowledge of the oil patch.

What was great was the fact there was no one in that room to question my knowledge of the oil industry. I had a wonderful audience. Absolutely no one tells a story like a rig hand — even a former rig hand like myself.

Chapter Twenty One

Fond Memories

HARDLY A DAY GOES BY now that I don't think of some incident that took place on a rig camp or that I don't think of someone I knew out there in the bush. It was sort of like a family unit out in camp. I had a lot of respect for the pushes who could control their men and get the best out of them. Most were uneducated, but they were practical and very, very wise. They had no formal training at all for their exceptional type of job, and some of the best I worked for were very young: still in their twenties or early thirties. They carried a huge responsibility for the safety and well-being of everyone in camp.

These very young men were in charge of a two or three million dollar operation under extreme conditions and were under pressure to complete a well on time and within budget. It was interesting to note that nearly all the best rig hands were raised on a farm or were still living on a farm. They seemed to be able to fix anything. In those early years, there were no formally trained electricians, plumbers, gas fitters, tinsmiths or mechanics. Everything was learned right there on the rig. By contrast, rig hands today are highly-trained experts, as most rigs are operated by computers.

I've stopped looking behind me now when I take my garbage out to the lane, and I hardly ever dream about grizzly bears any more. I don't worry about plane crashes in the wilderness, and I never use the word turbulence. I drive almost everywhere. I do look up once in awhile when I see a jet crossing the sky. Then I think about all those little planes and choppers in which I flew so many miles and in which I had so many terrifying or exciting adventures.

I don't worry about being stuck any more. British Columbia has great roads. But I still haven't removed my shovel, chains, battery boosters, or tow rope from the back of my pickup. I've been considering trading in my pickup for a car or van, but I don't know if I'm ready for that yet. My old pickup is my last link to the oil patch.

I still pack a lunch and fill a thermos of coffee when I visit my favourite fishing holes — even for a short trip up a mountain or down a back road.

I unpacked a box last week — one of the last boxes left from my move out to British Columbia. When I opened it, my mind filled with memories of the rig camps. There on the very top was a stack of company stickers and business cards, gin pads and an unopened deck of cards. The company logo only served to bring back more memories. I'd read where that particular service company had gone under, as so many had when the slump hit the oil industry in the early '80s. There will be no more of those gin pads or playing cards with that logo on them. I sat thinking about that company and some of the guys I knew who had worked for them.

One of them was Al. He'd spent 31 days on our rig on a fishing job one time. Everyone on that lease was short-tempered — that is, everyone except Al. He was always pleasant and treated our camp staff with a lot of respect.

The day he finished that job and mobiled for a chopper to pick him up, my crew and I were standing in our doorway waving good-bye. He ran up to the chopper, reached into the doorway, picked up a small parcel, and ran back with it. He thrust the parcel into my hands, and with a grin and a wink, he was gone. We watched him climb aboard, and we stood in the cold doorway as the little chopper flew away into the darkening sky. He was gone from our sight but not from our memories. You don't forget guys like Al.

We walked into camp and sat down to read our brand-new newspapers. Only a serviceman like Al knew how precious a newspaper was to those of us who were so isolated. There were a lot of men like Al. Real nice men who were genuine and sincere and who played their part in making camp life as good as possible under harsh conditions. And, there were quite a few of the other kind, like Dennis and . . . .

I've written about the hard drinking when the hands went to town. I don't know if people can understand why they drank. One has to experience that kind of life before passing judgment. Rig work is extremely dangerous.

I learned, early in my rig days, that one must go along with the flow or be left out of everything. I learned to sip on one drink all evening while I watched the rig hands enjoy a few hours away from camp. After the second round, no one noticed how much I was drinking anyway. All the guys in a crew would insist on buying the cook and helper a drink. It was wise not to refuse. I just let the waitress bring it and let one of the guys pay for it, and then, sooner or later, someone would drink it.

Sometimes I wondered why my helper and I went into town with the crew, especially when we'd often get stuck a mile from camp. They would all be out pushing while I drove. Surely it was time to reconsider and go back to camp, but we never did. I suspect one of the main reasons we were invited to go to town was that we could be relied upon to stay sober, and I could drive anyone's truck back to camp. I also know that if we hadn't gone along on those adventures I wouldn't have had much to write about.

We never accepted an invitation to go to town with a crew until we got to know them well. It doesn't take long to know if a crew is safe to go along with. Usually I felt very protected by the rig hands. We picked our friends very, very carefully on a rig camp.

There are two going-to-town rules: never refuse a drink, and don't nag about getting home on time. Many, many times we reached camp at daylight and had to scurry to get breakfast ready on time, but it was fun then and it is fun now to remember. No self-respecting rig hand is going to leave town until he's good and ready — even if it's two days later. Rig hands didn't worry then about getting fired, because getting fired, quitting a job, or being thrown into jail weren't really things to be concerned about during the oil patch boom years. There was always another job right down the road.

There were so many other incidents I haven't written about and people I haven't mentioned, like the old Native who worked derrick on a rig in the Red Earth area of northern Alberta. I could write a book on that man.

After three months on that rig camp, the only words I'd heard him utter were, "Good morning," "Good night," and "Pass the butter, please."

Then one beautiful spring morning when the sun was rising and I was yelling at my campy for sleeping in, that old Native showed up at the kitchen door. He stood around waiting for me to finish my tirade and then said, "Have you seen the sunrise this morning?"

I looked at him in astonishment! Then I looked at the campy with shame as we headed toward the east window. We didn't hear the old Native move, but I knew he was standing right behind me as we watched one of the most spectacular sunrises I'd ever seen. And then I turned around to face that old man who was still watching the sky. He had such a beautiful expression on his face. It was peace.

He didn't really need anything from camp. He'd just come down to make sure two busy people didn't miss one of Mother Nature's wonders. It's moments like that I remember. How could I ever forget men like that old Native? I can't remember his name, but I will always remember his face.

I still enjoy watching the sun rise and set, but not as often as I did on the rigs. I was up early then to see those incredible shows in the sky. I know why that old Native always worked derrick. The guys on that rig said they'd never known him to work any other job — always derrick. I like to speculate that he worked up there on ·

that platform, so high on the rig tower, to be a little closer to his God.

There is a voice in the wilderness that I keep hearing every time I am out in a wilderness fishing hole. It keeps calling me back, but I won't be going back. It's all memories now, fantastic memories that have provided so many pleasant thoughts for me over the years. And it has inspired me to write this book.

My grandchildren are all grown now, but they still like to listen when I begin to tell stories that start with, "When Grandma went to work on the oil rigs in high heels . . . ."

GLOSSARY
of unusual words or terms used in this book

BLOWOUT:

A blowout occurs while drilling is in progress thus the term blowout. When this occurs pipe, mud and sometimes oil will be forced out of the hole causing much destruction and sometimes deaths. Blowout Preventers, (BOPs) were developed as a means of preventing a blow out, but on occasion the pressure is so great it will cause a blowout even with the use of this equipment.

CAMP WATCH:

A drilling company will send a crew out to watch the camp for various reasons. One is to wait for decent roads, or spring road bans to come off the highways so they can move the camp and drilling rig. The whole move will involve up to 35 or 40 loads. The camp itself is six trailers plus the power plant shack, the propane tank and quite possibly another trailer brought in to house extra men at the end of the previous well. The rig is taken apart and requires many trips for it alone plus all the smaller trailers out at that lease, the pipe and rack, mud shack, power plant and anything else.

CAVE IN:

This occurs when the drill bit hits a hole deep in the earth. The drill bit just drops into a void that has to be filled before they can continue. Huge quantities of "stuff" are brought in and sent down the hole. Walnut shells are one such commodity, feathers are another, chunks of Styrofoam packing are used as well as drilling mud to fill the cavity. This is where I heard the term "cementing off" used and refer to when the void is filled enough for drilling to commence again.

COLORS:

Every drilling company has a chosen color that identifies it from all others. For example Peter Bawden Drilling paints all their trucks green; the rigs are green; jackets we received for safety days are green and so are the small flags posted along a road or trail leading into a new location. When a rig hand got fired or quit he would "change colors" so to speak when he hired on with another drilling company.

DERRICKMAN:

This is a very dangerous job performed on a heavy metal platform about three quarters of the way up the rig. The derrickman will be strapped in according to safety regulations. However, if a stand of pipe is not handled properly, it could knock him out of his perch or kill him. The men who work at this level of expertise are highly skilled men who rely on each other for their very lives.

DOGHOUSE:

This is the shack on the drilling platform where all the work is done, meals eaten and orders given. On most rigs I worked on the doghouse was an extension of the drill platform. It is shelter from the terrible cold of winter that Canadian rig hands face so many months a year while they perform their tasks out on the open drilling area. Some doghouses are neat and tidy and others are a real mess. All the years I worked on the rigs I never heard of a dog, as in animal, in the dog house.

DUMMY ROUGHNECK:

The very bottom man on the ladder or the pecking order on a crew. This man will be put to work at horrible jobs, mostly dirty work, will be sent on errands that will force him to run around all day looking for items that might not even exist. He will be the brunt of every man's ire or idea of a joke. He will be called stupid, fool, dummy until he shows the driller he just might make a roughy someday or he will quit and take up some other career. The first week of a dummy roughneck's life on a drilling lease will determine just what kind of a man he is.

ENGINEER:

Currently an engineer working on the rigs will hold a degree in Petroleum Engineering, but when I worked on the rigs almost every engineer was a former tool pusher hired by the oil company. The engineer is top dog, along with the geologist, on the whole operation. The oil company has secured the lease where they are drilling and they determine just where they will drill the well.

FISHERMAN:

Fishing is the term used when servicemen are brought in to retrieve an item that has been dropped down the hole. They will use specialized tools and in most cases it takes a long time and causes a lot of cussing, frustration and expense for the drilling company.

GEOLOGIST:

This man doesn't show up on a lease until the crew is spudded in and drilling is ready to begin. The geologist will determine what type of mud mixture will be used and he will determine the viscosity, (thickness) according to what they are drilling through. There is a huge difference between drilling through soft shale than hard rock, thus the difference in viscosity.

HOT SHOT COMPANY/DRIVER:

These are people we refer to as service people with headquarters in oil centers. They will deliver almost anything to a rig site any time of the day or night no matter how small or how big a machine they have to use to get said item in PDQ.

LOGGING:

This is a procedure done by a service company who will determine what is down the well. They have specialized tools that will be run down the hole bringing up a core sample which is then sent to the oil company's head office for examination and further instructions. It is an expensive procedure performed by highly trained technicians. The information in this core sample is the final result of the drilling of the well and is valuable to anyone wanting to sell it as written about in one chapter on oil espionage.

MOTORMAN:

Third man from the bottom. He will be on the platform with the other roughnecks when they are tripping, bringing the pipe out of the hole, when they must change bits, and when they are putting the pipe back into the hole. He is responsible for the maintenance of the motors that keep the whole operation going as nearly all drilling is out in the bush and not on a power line. He will also be responsible for maintenance of the power plant in camp and must make sure it is oiled, greased, coddled and that there is enough fuel at both power plants to last till the end of the well.

MUD:

There are two types of mud rig hands talk about, the terrible mud, or muddy conditions they work in most of the time and the mud they drill with. When I was on the rigs I was told most of the drilling mud was brought up from Utah, USA. When I asked the obvious question, "why can't you use some of this local mud, especially when there is so much of it?" I don't know if they have found the right type of mud in Canada yet, but I sure know there is one hell of a lot of mud in the oil patch, both in bags waiting to be used in the drilling of oil wells and on almost every road or trail leading into an oil lease.

RACKED RIG:

This' is a drilling rig that is "torn out," taken apart and ready to be relocated or stored according to the drilling company's wishes. If a rig is racked out in the bush, then the camp will probably left for camp watchers, or caretakers, until it can be hauled to the next drill site. When spring break-up occurs and the roads are shut down or restrictions are in effect, then many rigs were racked up and left in company yards in oil towns or back to head office yards for safekeeping, rebuilding or repair. During the 1980s and early 1990s many rigs were "racked" almost permanently as the oil patch came to a halt.

RICH OIL STRIKE:

This is an area where surveying and geology test show there is a possibility of oil, gas or both. Then a rig is brought in to drill a test well so when tests show they have a very good producer or they have a gusher or a blow-out then this is a RICH OIL STRIKE. The owners of this wildcat well will probably have put up "tight hole" signs during the last phase of drilling. They want to be the first to sign a lease on the properties surrounding their rich oil strike thus they do not want to share information obtained during the testing and final analysis of their wildcat well.

RIG HANDS, SERVICE HANDS CAMP CREWS:

I do not know why rig hands are called rig hands but they are, and anyone coming into camp to perform a job is referred to as a service hand. I have been told the expression "hands" when talking about oil patch workers is an American or "Yankee" term. Camp crew are the cook, helper and camp attendant.

ROUGHNECK:

Roughy, Dummy, Hey You and several other just awful names when everyone is shouting for him at the same time. It will be to perform a task, always a very dirty job, a job that no one else with any self respect would offer to do except of course the Dummy Roughneck. This man will be one small step above the Dummy Roughneck as there is always two roughnecks to a crew.

SOUR GAS:

Natural gas that has a high percentage of hydrogen sulfide It is extremely poisonous and workers must wear gas masks when working with this gas. Sour gas is cleaned up at the refinery by removing the sulfur, that yellow stuff we see in huge piles near gas plants or refineries.

SPUDDED IN:

This is the actual beginning of drilling, the very first strike into the ground designated by the geologists and surveyors who tested the areas prior to securing the drilling lease for that property.

STUCK IN THE HOLE:

This occurs when they can't go up or down and may have torn the bit out. That's when they bring in all those high priced men with special equipment and tools to retrieve the broken bit and get on with the job.

TIGHT HOLE:

This is the term used to warn anyone entering a drilling lease that they are not welcome. Signs will be posted on turn-off roads and at the entrance to camp and drill site where final testing is being performed to determine what is down the well.

TOOL PUSH:

Push, Tool Pusher, Tooly, Dad or several other names used to describe the man who is in charge of the entire drilling operation. The drilling company owns the drilling rig and the camp which is hired by an oil company to drill a well on a specific lease. He is responsible for three shifts of rig hands, 10

dryhole – P9D

people, the cook, cook's helper and the camp attendant. On occasion there will be another rig hand called a lease hound and on occasion there will be an assistant driller. A Tool Push is a rig hand who has worked his way up the ladder from roughneck or, in some cases a dummy roughneck. He is The Boss on the drilling rig platform and in camp.

TRIPPING:

This is the process of changing a worn drill bit. When a rig is drilling through especially hard rock formations, it's not unusual for them to go through a diamond - real diamond- drill bit every few hours. This involves taking stands of pipe out of the well and standing them in the rig. As each pipe is removed from the stem of the well, the derrickman ties it in place high up in the derrick and secures it to the rig platform as well. The worn out bit is removed, and a new one is put on before the pipe is all put back into the hole, one length at a time.

WILDCAT WELL:

This is a well that is being drilled in new territory.

To order:

TERROR IN THE OIL PATCH
HIGH HEELS 'N' OIL RIGS

Fill out order form and send with cheque or money order payable to:
Bev Jones
c/o Joyce Ann Publications
381 Norton Street, Penticton, British Columbia, V2A 4H9
Phone (250) 490-9639
Fax (250) 492-7278

	QTY	EACH	TOTAL
TERROR IN THE OIL PATCH		12.95	
HIGH HEELS 'N' OIL RIGS		12.95	
Shipping & Handling (one book)			2.75
Shipping & Handling (up to 5 books)			5.50
TOTAL ENCLOSED			

✂ --

To order:

TERROR IN THE OIL PATCH
HIGH HEELS 'N' OIL RIGS

Fill out order form and send with cheque or money order payable to:
Bev Jones
c/o Joyce Ann Publications
381 Norton Street, Penticton, British Columbia, V2A 4H9
Phone (250) 490-9639
Fax (250) 492-7278

	QTY	EACH	TOTAL
TERROR IN THE OIL PATCH		12.95	
HIGH HEELS 'N' OIL RIGS		12.95	
Shipping & Handling (one book)			2.75
Shipping & Handling (up to 5 books)			5.50
TOTAL ENCLOSED			

PLEASE SEND BOOKS ORDERED TO:

Name: _____

Street: _____

City: _____

Province/
State: _____   Postal Code/
                                Zip: _____

✂ --

PLEASE SEND BOOKS ORDERED TO:

Name: _____

Street: _____

City: _____

Province/
State: _____   Postal Code/
                                Zip: _____